POWER
FOR THE
PIONEERS
THE GREEN & E.N.V. AERO ENGINES

A. E. TAGG

© A.E. Tagg

First Published 1990

Published & Printed by
Crossprint, Daish Way,
Dodnor Industrial Estate,
Newport, Isle of Wight.

ISBN 1 872981 01 1

CONTENTS

ACKNOWLEDGEMENTS

A work of this type makes considerable use of photographs, whose origins have inevitably become obscured with the passage of time. The present custodians of many of those used have performed a valuable service to present and future generations interested in early aviation in all its aspects. The author would like to thank all of these and their predecessors, without whom a great deal of knowledge would be lost.

Large organisations include the Science, Royal Air Force, Fleet Air Arm and Imperial War Museums, The Royal Scottish Museum and the Royal Aerospace Establishment. The early aviation press, particularly Flight, Aero and The Aeroplane are great sources of information. The Jack M. Bruce/G. Stuart Leslie collection was invaluable as was individual help from Mike Goodall, Philip Jarrett, John Bagley, George Cull, Brian Kervell, the late H.F. Cowley and members of the Cody, Cooke and Green families.

A special mention must be made of the late Joe Gascoyne who corresponded with enthusiasm and whom I was fortunate enough to meet before his death in 1972, for he was there when it was all happening and closely involved with the E.N.V. engines and their users at the time.

POWER FOR THE PIONEERS
The Green & E.N.V. Aero Engines

Introduction

Success or failure for the pioneer aviators depended to a large degree on the availability of a suitable power plant. The adaptation of existing types of automobile and marine engines could not solve the problem of weight reduction which now became of particular significance. The achievement of light weight coupled with higher power output, that is an improved power to weight ratio, became the major contribution by the engine manufacturers towards achieving the possibility of flight. When this stage had been passed there was a need for progressive improvement to enhance the flight capabilities and particularly mechanical reliability.

Two British companies which were responsible for the production of water-cooled engines specifically for aviation use were Green and E.N.V. These two concerns competed for success in the earliest aeronautical activities in Edwardian Brit-ain, well before the outbreak of the First World War. Both suffered the competition of the lighter, but oil and fuel extravagant, air-cooled rotaries and to a lesser degree such water-cooled types as the Wolseley, N.E.C., Humber, ABC and Sun-beam, nevertheless they made a major contribution to the development of aviation in Britain, and also abroad, in the case of the E.N.V. Each achieved a measure of success but this had diminished well before 1914, although the Green won a major competition held in May of that year and continued to be manufactured in wartime. This was on a limited scale and the type found little use in aeroplanes, the main applications being in airships and coastal motor boats (C.M.B's).

The small Green engine had the distinction of again being put into production soon after the war for the civilian light plane market, some ten years after its original design.

For the R.N.A.S.– A batch of Green Engines ready for delivery

Gustavus Green
11th March 1865 - 29th December 1965

Advertisement
The Aero *May 1912*

Part 1 Gustavus Green and His Engines

Gustavus Green was born at Hounslow in Middlesex on the 11th March 1865 and commenced work at the age of 13. In his early days he was a hairdresser and wig maker and spent some time in the jewellery trade. He received no engineering training but with an innate mechanical ability he could design and make mechanical devices of various types. In 1897 he moved to Bexhill in Sussex where he established a cycle-making and repair business in Weston Road and undertook engineering work for local concerns, becoming involved with motor-driven vehicles in the early 1900's. By 1904-5 he was taking out patents on various ideas for petrol engines and was offering his single-cylinder water-cooled engine with integral radiators for use in motor-cycles and tri-cars which was the basis of this expanding business and necessitated moving into larger premises in Reginald and Victoria Roads. By 1904 he had embarked on motor car building, his first being supplied to a Dr. Miller and his second to Lord Francis Hope, who gave his name to the famous diamond.

The second car, with a 26-30 HP four cylinder engine, was exhibited in chassis form at the Motor Show of March 1906 held at the Agricultural Hall, Islington. The vehicle incorporated a number of original features in the design of both the chassis and the engine, some of which in the latter being employed later in the aviation engines. The overhead valves, detachable complete with their seatings, and the sheet metal water jackets, sealed at the lower end with a rubber ring, were both carried forward, the latter changed to copper whereas those on the car were made from brass sheet. The novel system of valve operation by means of a camshaft only 3 1/2" long, low down at the front of the engine and operating the valves through a series of torque shafts, levers and pull rods, was not perpetuated.

Colonel Capper, commandant of the Balloon School and Factory at Farnborough, visited the show and was impressed by the engine in the Green car and arranged for a developed version, a 90° V8 of 80HP to be designed for use in an airship already under consideration. A contract for the Green engine was placed in 1908 for use in the airship Nulli Secundus but trouble with this caused it to be transferred to Dirigible No. II, later named Gamma, which was eventually launched in February 1910 and was the first British-built airship to fly with a British engine. It was operated by the Army, after completion of its trials, until early 1911, when two 48 HP Iris engines designed by Geoffrey de Havilland replaced the Green, these presumably being judged more efficient.

Mr. Green was sufficiently competent to manufacture virtually the entire car in his own works including making his own forgings and casting patterns. He continued to manufacture the motor cycle engine in two sizes, supplying this to such firms as Regal, Ivy and Zenith, the 499 cc Regal-Green breaking records for the flying mile and kilometre at Brooklands in solo and sidecar form in 1912 and 1913. The smaller single cylinder engine rated at 2 3/4 HP was incorporated into the Green-Mackie alternator unit for providing electrical power for radio in aircraft or airships, and was displayed on the Green stand at the Aero Show at Olympia in March 1914. However, the airship engine was a considerably bigger manufacturing proposition and the V8 was sub-contracted to an established manufacturer in Wolverhampton after preparation of the design. Subcontracting of manufacture of complete engines to well established engineering concerns was to become the normal means of production for Green aircraft engines.

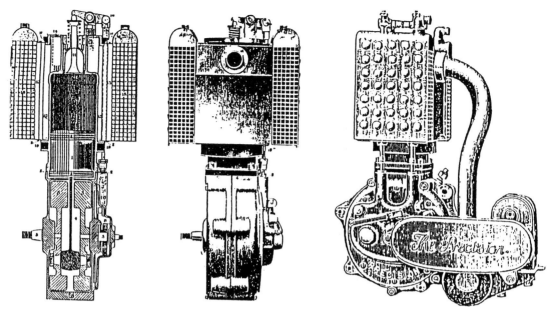

The Green single cylinder motorcycle engine, *the basis for all future developments*

The Green car with four cylinder engine
As exhibited in March 1906 at the Motor Show held at the Agricultural Hall Islington

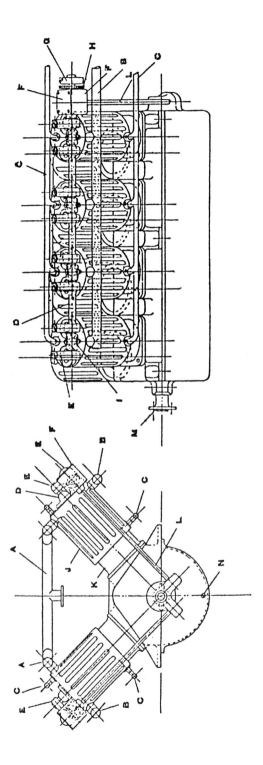

Green's Motor Patents Syndicate. Ltd.

GENERAL ARRANGEMENT

or

... 80 B.H.P. PETROL ENGINE ...

References to Letters on General Arrangement

A and A1—Induction pipes.

B—Exhaust pipes.

C and C1—Circulating water pipes.

D—Bonnet-caps for valve springs.

E and E1—Overhead valve actuating gear.

F—Bevel gear box for driving camshaft.

G—Distributor or contact breaker.

H—Magneto gear wheel or timing wheel.

I—Bracket carrying cam case.

J—Embossed copper water jacket.

K—Cylinder.

L—Vertical cam driving shaft.

M—Flange coupling.

N—Oil drain screw.

80 H.P. Green.V.8 1908

The 80.H.P.Green.V.8. installed in the airship Gamma
The engine is fitted across the car with extension shafts for two swivelling propellers

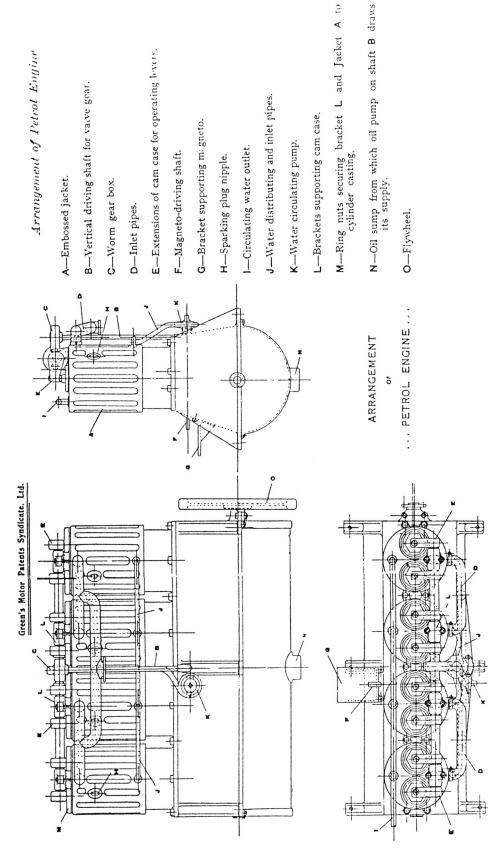

Arrangement of Petrol Engine

A—Embossed jacket.

B—Vertical driving shaft for valve gear.

C—Worm gear box.

D—Inlet pipes.

E—Extensions of cam case for operating levers.

F—Magneto-driving shaft.

G—Bracket supporting magneto.

H—Sparking plug nipple.

I—Circulating water outlet.

J—Water distributing and inlet pipes.

K—Water circulating pump.

L—Brackets supporting cam case.

M—Ring nuts securing bracket L and Jacket A to cylinder casting.

N—Oil sump from which oil pump on shaft B draws its supply.

O—Flywheel.

Green's Motor Patents Syndicate. Ltd.

ARRANGEMENT
or
... PETROL ENGINE ...

30/35. H.P. Green 1908

10

THE OVERHEAD VALVE GEAR.

ELEVATION.

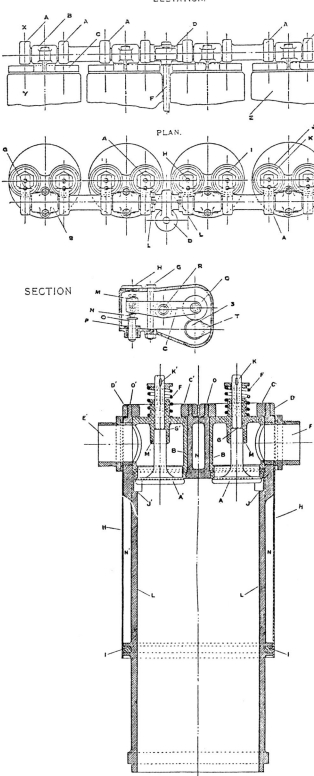

PLAN.

SECTION

Overhead Valve Gear :

A—Extensions carrying levers.

B—Bracket supporting cam-case.

C—Ring nuts securing Bracket B to cylinder.

D—Worm case, containing upper worm and wheel.

E—Cylinder.

F—Vertical driving shaft, rotating camshaft.

G—Bolt holding two halves of cam case together.

H—Screw plug giving access to adjusting screw of levers.

I—Bonnetted cap nuts over valve springs and stems.

J—Ring nuts securing bracket B to cylinder.

K—Cylinder casting.

L—Steel stops for limiting swinging of cam case.

M—Locking nut to adjusting screw.

N—Adjusting screw.

O—Tappet pin for valve stems.

P—Steel guide to tappet pin O.

Q—Bolt holding two halves of cam case together.

R—Pivot for levers.

S—Cam shaft.

T—Cam.

U—Levers for actuating valves.

Reference Letters to Illustration :

CYLINDER.

A—Valves.

B—Cages.

C—Keep rings to cages for valves.

D—Keep rings to jackets.

E—Inlet and exhaust part nipples.

F—Valve springs.

G—Recesses to receive upper part of valve stems.

H—Copper jacket,

I—Indiarubber ring.

J—Recess to prevent valve head falling into cylinder.

K—Cotter securing spring.

L—Body of cylinder.

30/35. H.P. Green 1908

At the same time as the V8 was being developed, a four cylinder upright engine of 30/35 HP for aircraft use was also designed at the suggestion of Wilbur Wright with whom Green had been in touch and both these engines were described in a brochure prepared by Green's Motor Patents Syndicate Ltd. and circulated in 1908, claiming to be "the first practicable motor that has yet appeared for aerial navigation". The Managing Director of the Syndicate was Mr J Miller. The business later traded under the name of the Green Engine Co. from the middle of 1911 and "Commodore" Fred May became Chairman and is believed to have provided finance for its expansion.

The two engine types had many features in common, both having overhead inlet and exhaust valves mounted parallel to each other in cages incorporating the seatings. The operation was by overhead camshaft by way of rockers carrying rollers at the camshaft end and through tappets to the valve. The whole of the valve mechanism was enclosed in cast aluminium, oil-tight casings that could be released and swung clear to enable the valve cages to be removed without disturbing the timing. The valvecages were retained by dome-shaped nuts with apertures for inspection of tappet clearances.

The cylinder head and barrel were made in one piece which was machined all over from a steel casting, a recess in the head adjacent to the valves being designed to trap the valve and prevent it falling into the cylinder in the event of a breakage. A groove was machined on the outside of the barrel to accept the rubber sealing ring that formed the patented watertight joint at the lower end of the helmet-shaped copper water jacket, the jacket being held down by screwed locking rings fitted to the outside of the valve ports. The unions for the water connections on the sides also clamped the water jacket to the cylinder through the medium of radiussed washers to ensure a close fit for water-tightness. This early brochure describes pressed copper jackets with embossed flutes, but the flutes were soon deleted and it is believed in production the jackets were produced by spinning. Cast aluminium brackets bolted to the cylinder heads housed the bearings for the camshaft. The original scheme for releasing the camshaft casings, consisting of two screws, must have proved to be unsatisfactory and was superseded by individual clamps on each cylinder, held down by a wing-nut. On the 60 HP and larger engines, which came later, an aid to starting was provided in the form of exhaust valve lifters operated by quick-thread pins in the camshaft casings, working from a unified control.

The upper camshaft drive was originally by skew gearing, soon replaced by bevel gearing, which in the case of the four cylinder engine was by vertical drive shaft between numbers 2 and 3 cylinders. The drive was at the rear on the V8 and was also transferred to the rear on later production engines of all types. On some engines a drive for an r.p.m. indicator or a distributor was provided on the top of the casing.

The camshaft was carried in plain white metalled phosphor bronze bearings at either end and between each throw in a cast aluminium crankcase forming the upper half of the crank chamber. Ball bearing thrust races were introduced in a housing at the forward end of the crankcase, after some early engines had shown the need, and catered for pusher and tractor applications. The use of extended bolts to clamp the crankshaft bearings through the crankcase and the cylinder holding down flanges was claimed as a means of obtaining rigidity in the design despite the use of a relatively light crankcase. The cylinders were closely spaced and were held down by five bolts each, the adjacent cylinder flanges containing half a hole only and sharing a common fixing. Steel connecting rods with white metal big end bearings were used; the gudgeon pins were pinned to the small ends and worked in bronze bushes in the cast iron pistons.

The lower half was a sheet aluminium tray with cast aluminium ends held up by bolts and metal straps, with a small central sump from which the lubricating oil was drawn by scavenge pump driven from the lower end of the vertical drive shaft, which also pumped the oil to the bearings through ways cast in the crankcase. The cylinders received lubricant by splash from the crankshaft, supplemented on later engines by external pipes feeding from the main oil passage to small holes in the cylinder walls. The casings of the camshaft and valve gear were filled separately with oil sufficient for 30 hours running; on the four, six and eight cylinder types the cases covered pairs of cylinders, but on the V12 individual casings for each cylinder were provided. Funnel-like ventilators were introduced to reduce the crankcase pressure to about 5 psi to minimise leakage from joints and in some instances the oil mist was directed into the carburettor intake.

A cross-shaft driven by skew gearing at the rear of the engine drove the magneto and water-pump. On a few early 35 HP engines the magneto was mounted on a platform level with the cylinder heads and was driven from the gearbox at the top

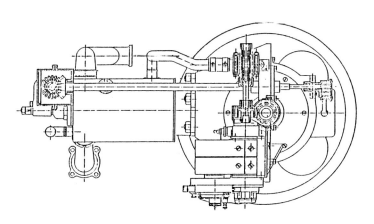

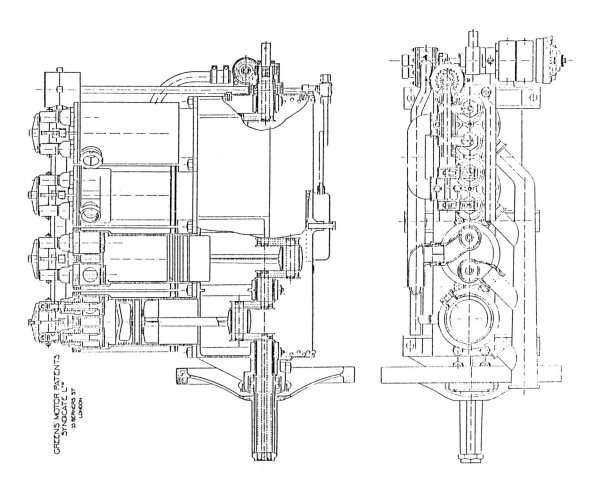

GRENS' MOTOR PATENTS
SYNDICATE LTD
33 BERNERS ST
LONDON

1910 35. H.P. Green aviation engine,
The type from which the larger aviation and marine engines were developed

13

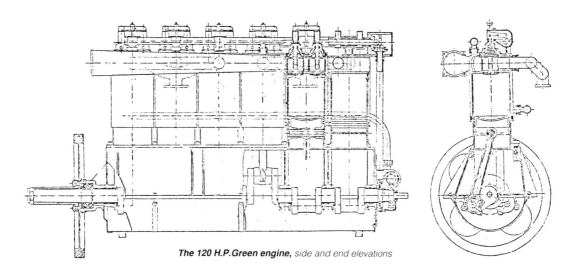

The 120 H.P.Green engine, *side and end elevations*

A six cylinder 100. H.P. engine, *This surviving engine on display at Yeovilton is identified C.6.No.7 also 6.100.G. No.2615.w*

Green's engineering works, *Victoria Road, Bexhill*

of the vertical shaft. The water-pump, originally a rotary type, soon replaced by a geared type, carried the coolant through an external copper pipe to the lower end of each water jacket. The joints were originally made by hose and clips but improved water connections with mechanical unions were introduced considerably later.

An external flywheel was provided adjacent to the crankshaft extension, a precaution against crankshaft vibration arising from propeller flutter or misfiring, although this was often discarded, a weight saving of 23 1/2lbs to the 30/35 HP and 37lbs to the 60/80 HP engine.

A cast induction manifold carried an updraught carburettor - a Green patented type originally, with vaporisation of the fuel aided by the adjacent coolant pipe, but this was generally superseded by Zenith types. Two carburettors were fitted to the six cylinder and four to the V12 types. Extra power was obtained by drilling of the cylinder barrels; five 10mm holes raising the power of the 60 HP engine to 80 HP.

This description is basically applicable to the whole range of Green engines that were evolved from the four in-line and V8 engines of 1908, which included six in-line and 60° V12 types of up to 300 HP by 1915.

By early in 1908 Gustavus Green had transferred his original London Office from Kimberley House, 14/17 Holborn Viaduct to 55 Berners Street and it was from there and later from 166 Piccadilly that business and sales were conducted. In 1913 he acquired premises in Twickenham, Middlesex and moved to Pelham House, 97 Strawberry Vale, but still retained property in Bexhill including the Victoria Road workshop, later used for motor-cycle work as Green's Engineering Works by his Son Charles between 1926 and 1933. The Twickenham works at 4 Edwin Road was used for development and prototype manufacture but production of both types of four cylinder engines was entirely sub-contracted, initially to the Aster Engineering Co. of Wembley, deliveries of whose first batch commenced in July 1909 under the supervision of Mr P V Cook with whom a close association developed. Gustavus Green himself was undoubtedly the inspiration for the general design, although this was contested by a former draughtsman in a letter to the "Aero" dated 1st February 1910. Alexander G Clark claimed responsibility for the design and conceded "improvements only" to Gustavus Green. A letter from the Company Secretary E C Hide refuted the claim the following week, stating that, as an employee, Clark had been engaged to carry our Mr

Green's instructions. The Company's views were well supported by the Editor, C G Grey.

In 1909 the company exhibited at the first Aero Show held at Olympia in March and again at the Paris Show in September. At Olympia there were two machines intended to use Green engines which were shown in an incomplete state. These were the Short No. 1 biplane for which, according to "Flight", a 30 HP type was planned and a strange device for rising vertically called the Lamplough Orthopter which was to use a 50 HP Green. The Short, with Frank McClean in control, unsuccessfully attempted flight with other engines owing to late availability of the Green and no more was heard of the Lamplough. It was Short No. 2 which was flown in September 1909 with a Vivinus engine and soon re-engined with a 50/60 HP Green, that mounted the first Green engine to be airborne, when Moore-Brabazon won the Daily Mail prize of £1000 for a flight of one mile in a closed circuit on the 30th October 1909; he followed this in March 1910 by taking the British Michelin Cup and £500 prize with a flight of 19 miles in the same machine until the winning flight was brought to a premature end when the crankshaft burst through the crankcase; longer flights had been made before unofficially.

Robert Blackburn was among the first to acquire a 35 HP Green and used it in the first Blackburn aeroplane, the unsuccessful monoplane completed in September 1909, which was abandoned after failing to achieve flight.

S F Cody's first machine, developed from the British Army Aeroplane, was powered by either Antoinette or E.N.V. French made engines, but his second machine, which appeared in June 1910, was intended to compete in competitions for which an all-British machine was required. He designed it to use two 60 HP Green engines but could only afford one with which he flew tentatively until he crashed on the 26th on Laffans Plain. Despite injury, he recovered sufficiently to attend the Bournemouth Meeting in the middle of the next month but could achieve brief flights only on two days and won no prizes. In August he took the machine to Lanark for the meeting held between the 5th and the 13th. The Green Company had supplied the second engine with an offer to purchase at a discount or to return it after the meeting with limitations on its usage at Lanark. In the event he could not get the two engines to synchronise and damage was caused to the chain drive. Shortly after this he negotiated terms with the E.N.V. company for the loan of the new British E.N.V. Type F and was given terms which allowed for its use for the Baron de Forest and Michelin Contests. The press reports show he used an E.N.V. from Tuesday to the conclusion of the meeting, which was said to be the one used in the previous year, namely the French Type C. A further note in "Aero" of the 5th October reports him flying at Aldershot on the 30th September with the French engine and this was confirmed in a note on the 23rd November reporting that he had changed in the previous week to a British E.N.V. In the description of the machine in "Flight" in the issues of 12th and 19th November, photographs show an E.N.V. seemingly the borrowed Type F. He was using the 60 HP Green when, on the 4th November, he flew for 2 hours 24 1/2 mins, a distance of 94 1/2 miles, as his first attempt to take the British Empire Michelin Trophy. He was also using the Green for his flights of the 22nd December and the successful flight of the 31st December 1910 of 185 1/2 miles in 4 hours 47 mins., when he won the trophy and £500. He again won the No. 1 prize in 1911 with 261 miles and took the No. 2 Cup for a circuit flight in 1911, repeating this in 1912 using

a 100 HP Green in his earlier type machine. His completion of the Circuit of Britain flight in 1911, although overshadowed by the foreign competition, was a triumph for the Green engine, which was the only British engine to complete the course.

Cody constantly pressed for more power for his large machines and turned to the 120 HP Austro-Daimler for the Military Trials as the larger Green engines were not then available, although he continued to use Green engines for general work and for all British contests until his death in August 1913.

A 100 HP Green engine also powered the Grahame-White Charabanc which took the Michelin No. 1 Trophy in 1913 piloted by R H Carr, this engine having been acquired by Grahame-White from Cody's estate.

It is interesting to note that six out of seven British Empire Michelin Trophies Nos. 1 & 2 awarded between 1909 and 1913 were won on aircraft powered by Green engines. The sole exception was the A.B.C. powered Sopwith-Wright flown by Hawker.

The two civilians with naval officers are on the left Gustavus Green, Technical Director and Fred May, Chairman of the Company. The officers are Lieutenants Knobbs, Villiers and Burke

British Empire Michelin Trophies & Prizes

NO. 1 PEGASUS BY P MOREAU-VAUTIER	NO.2 'WINGED BLACKSMITH'
1909 (For completion by 31.3.1910) £500 J T C Moore-Brabazon on 1.3.1910 for a flight of 19 miles Short no. 2.60 HP Green	
1910 S F Cody on 31.12.1910 for a £500 flight of 185.46 miles in 4 hrs. 47 mins. in a closed circuit. Cody IIC Biplane 60 HP Green	INTRODUCED FOR COMPETITION IN 1911
1911 S F Cody on 29.10.1911 for a £500 flight of 261.5 miles in 5 hrs. 15 mins. in a closed circuit. Cody III Biplane. 60 HP Green	1911 S F Cody on 11.9.1911 for a £400 125 mile circuit from Laffans Plain, Andover, Hendon, Brooklands, Laffans Plain in 3 hrs. 6 1/2 mins. Cody III Biplane. 60 HP Green
1912 H G Hawker on 24.10.1912 for £500 a flight of 8 hrs. 23 mins. over Brooklands. Sopwith-Wright Biplane 40 HP A.B.C.	1912 S F Cody on 12.12.1912 for a £600 186 mile circuit from Laffans Plain, Larkhill (Southampton), Newhaven, Brooklands, Laffans Plain in 3 hrs. 26 mins. Diversion due to fog. Cody VC Biplane. 100 HP Green
1913 R H Carr on 6.11.1913 for a £500 flight Hendon-Brooklands alighting every 60 miles. Total 300 miles. Grahame-White Biplane. 100 HP Green	1913 £800 NOT AWARDED.

The 100H.P. Green installed in the Grahame-White biplane in which R.H.Carr, seen here with mechanic Chapman, won the Michelin Trophy No.1 in 1913

British Empire Michelin Trophy No.2 *won by S.F. Cody in both 1911 and 1912*

British Empire Michelin Trophy No.1 *The example shown was won by H.G. Hawker in 1912*

Gustavus Green only ever flew once and this was as Cody's passenger on the 6th August 1913, the day before the crash in which Cody and his passenger died. Cody and Green were on good terms and met quite often in the course of their affairs, Cody calling him "Greeny Boy" and Green, who thought Cody "a funny fellow" on first acquaintance, later described him as "a good sort when you got to know him".

Green engines were used to power some of Sopwith's early aircraft, flown with some success by H G Hawker. In June 1913 the 100 HP Bat Boat took the Mortimer Singer Prize for amphibians and in the following August the 100 HP floatplane completed 1043 miles around the coast of Britain. The flight terminated near Dublin, when Hawker made an emergency landing resulting in severe damage. The crash was reputedly caused by his foot slipping off the rudder bar on the approach to the landing. The reason for landing was to inspect the engine as rattles had developed which, it was suspected, were broken valve springs. A few miles further to Dublin and the fliers would have found Gustavus Green waiting with replacements. Although the flight failed in the object of completing the full course for the Daily Mail £5000 Prize, it was recognised as a great feat by both men and machine meriting the award of a consolation prize of £1000.

The Green-engined Sopwith Circuit seaplane was reconstructed as a landplane with which Hawker made attempts to gain the 1913 Michelin prizes. He was forced to retire feeling unwell after 3 hours flying in his first attempt in October and was forced to give up due to bad weather on a second attempt, leaving Carr the winner of the No. 1 prize on the Grahame-White. He fared no better in his first attempt for the No. 2 prize in November, for, although he flew for 5 hours, he could not complete the course and was forced to land due to fuel leakage. A second attempt on the last day of the contest had to be abandoned due to fog after 3/4 hour and the prize was not awarded.

A V Roe was a leading user of the 35 HP in his triplanes and early biplanes in 1910-12 and his Mercury Triplane which flew in March 1910 at Brooklands was probably the first machine in which this engine was airborne, A V Roe was responsible for the first sale of a Green engine abroad when the Harvard Aeronautical Society bought one of his triplanes in 1910. He also used the 60 HP in his enclosed biplane, entered in the Military Trials of August 1912. F P Raynham flew this aircraft to establish a short-lived duration record of 7 hrs. 31 mins. in October.

Aviation was being encouraged by the offer of trophies and prize money by various companies and organisations. A well-known private individual, Patrick Y Alexander, put up £1000 for a British engine able to run for 24 hours giving an output of 35 HP. Of the five entrants other than the Green, only the Humber and Wolseley were submitted to the N.P.L. at Teddington for test in October 1910 and both failed. The Green was by far the most successful for it did run for 24 hours, but output at 31.5 HP at 1213 rpm was below the requirement so the prize was not awarded although a consolation prize of £200 was given. The second Alexander Competition, now open to motors of 40 to 75 HP from any country, was held at Farnborough in October 1911. Seven manufacturers entered but only the 60/65 HP Green and the E.N.V. engines were presented for test, the Green completing the two twelve-hour runs without stop or attention, recording 61.6 BHP at 1150 rpm. Other tests included tilting about longitudinal and transverse axes at 15° and a maximum power run of seven minutes during which 67.8 BHP was developed. This was a good performance which won the company the £1000 prize and enabled it to claim that it was "Britain's Best". A detailed report was published in "Flight" of the 24th February 1912.

The Naval and Military Aero Engine Competition held at Farnborough in 1914 started in May but the tests were delayed due to problems which arose on some of the early engine runs, attributed to the poorly designed testing equipment provided by the Royal Aircraft Factory. Of the 26 engines which arrived 13 withdrew before the start of the tests. Eight engines performed successfully the six hour eliminating trial and received awards of from £100 to £300, but of these engines it was the 100 HP six cylinder Green that triumphed and was awarded the £5000 prize by the War Office in October. The engines which passed the eliminating trials and provided competition to the Green were the Argyll sleeve-valve engine, the Beardmore-built Austro-Daimler, the Anzani, the Salmson water-cooled radial, the Sunbeam, the Wolseley and the Gnome rotary.

In September 1913, a proposal was made to restructure the company and a prospectus for the Green Engine Co. (1913) Ltd. with capital of £50,000 was issued. T. O. M. Sopwith and S. D Begbie, Managing Director of Aster Engineering, were invited to join the board. These changes did not come about and the company continued in its previous form and presumably raised funds by other means. In early 1941 the company had

1914
NAVAL AND MILITARY AEROPLANE ENGINE COMPETITION.—PARTICULARS OF ENGINES.

No.	Maker	B.H.P.	Revs. per min.	Cyl. No.	Bore (mm.)	Stroke (mm.)	Arrangement	Material	Jacket	Stroke/Bore ratio	Piston displacement per min. per B.H.P. (litres)	Piston speed (ft. per min.)	Weight Complete with all accessories ex radiator (lbs.)	Weight per B.H.P. (lbs.)	Fuel consumption (pints)	Lubrication	Ignition	Carburettor	Main bearings	Valve Position Inlet	Valve Position Exhaust	Valve How operated Inlet	Valve How operated Exhaust
	Air-cooled.																						
1	Anzani ...	125	1250	10	115	155	Rad.	C.I.	—	1·35	3·42	1270	464	3·77	0·7	P.	Bosch	Zenith	Ball	Head	Head	A	R. & P.R.
2	British rotary	100	1100	10	124	140	Rot.	St.	—	1·13	3·73	1010	—	—	—	—	—	—	—	—	—	—	—
3	Gnome (2) ...	105	1200	9	110	150	Rot.	St.	—	1·36	2·93	1180	275	2·62	0·73	P.	Bosch	Special	Ball	Walls	Head	Piston	R. & P.R.
4	Hart ...	150	1600	9	5″	6″	Rot.	St.	—	1·20	3·70	1600	—	—	—	P.	—	—	Ball	Head	Head	Auto	R. & P.R.
5	Hardy and Padmore	100	—	5	4″	4″	Rad.	—	—	1·0	—	—	—	—	—	—	—	—	—	—	—	—	—
6	Isaacson ...	100	1200	9	120	150	Rot.	St.	—	1·25	3·66	1180	250	2·50	—	P.	Bosch	Zenith	Ball	Piston	Head	Mech.	R. & P.R.
7	,, ...	200	1200	18	120	150	Rot.	St.	—	1·25	3·66	1180	465	2·32	—	P.	Bosch	Zenith	Ball	Piston	Head	Mech.	R. & P.R.
8	Wolseley (semi)	90	1800‡	8	4″	5½″	Vee	St.	—	1·37	3·61	1650	385	4·28	0·7	D.P.	Bosch	Claudel	W.M.	Head	Head	R. & P.R.	R. & P.R.
	Water-cooled.																						
9	Argylls (2) ...	130	1300	6	125	175	Vert.	St.	St.W.	1·40	2·8	1490	600†	4·61	0·55	F.&T.	Bosch	Zenith	W.M.	Sleeve valve			
10	Beardmore	90	1300	6	120	140	Vert.	C.I.	C.E.	1·17	2·73	1280	375	4·17	0·6	F.&T.	Bosch	A.D.	W.M.	Head	Head	R. & P.R.	R. & P.R.
11	Aus.-Daim.	120	1200	6	130	175	Vert.	C.I.	C.E.	1·35	2·79	1370	500	4·17	0·6	F.&T.	Bosch	A.D.	W.M.	Head	Head	R. & P.R.	R. & P.R.
12	Centrum*	150	900	6	150	140	Rad.	—	—	0·94	1·78	830	—	—	—	—	—	—	—	—	—	—	—
13	Dudbridge Ironworks	95	1250	7	120	140	Rad.	St.	C.B.	1·17	2·92	1150	375	3·95	0·6	P.	Bosch	Zenith	Ball	Head	Head	R. & P.R.	R. & P.R.
14	,, ,,	130	1250	9	120	140	Rad.	St.	C.B.	1·17	2·74	1150	465	3·57	0·6	P.	Bosch	Zenith	Ball	Head	Head	R. & P.R.	R. & P.R.
15	,, ,,	200	1250	14	120	140	Rad.	St.	C.B.	1·17	2·77	1150	660	3·30	0·6	P.	Bosch	Zenith	Ball	Head	Head	R. & P.R.	R. & P.R.
16	E.N.V. ...	100	1620§	8	95	165	Vee	St.	C.E.	1·74	3·04	1750	450†	4·50	0·6	P.	Bosch	Smith or Zenith	Ball	Head	Head	Direct	Direct
17	Green	120	1250	6	140	152	Vert.	St.	C.R.	1·08	2·94	1250	440	3·67	0·56	F.F.	Bosch	Zenith	W.M.	Head	Head	O.R.	O.R.
18	Sunbeam (2)	135	2000‡	8	90	150	Vee	C.I.	C.E.	1·66	2·27	1970	480	3·56	0·6	P.	Bosch	Claudel	W.M.	Side	Side	R.	R.
19	White & Poppe	130	1200	8	120	160	Vee	—	—	1·33	2·68	—	—	—	—	—	—	—	—	—	—	—	—
20	Wolseley ...	90	1800‡	8	3¾″	5½″	Vee	St.	C.S.	1·46	3·18	1650	405	4·50	0·65	D.P.	Bosch	Claudel	W.M.	Head	Head	R. & P.R.	R. & P.R.
21	,, ,,	130	1200	8	5″	7″	Vee	St.	C.S.	1·40	3·32	1400	720	5·54	0·63	D.P.	Bosch	Wolseley	W.M.	Head	Head	R. & P.R.	R. & P.R.
22	Wessex ...	130	2200	6	105	150	Vert.	—	—	1·43	2·64	2160	—	—	—	—	—	—	—	—	—	—	—

* Two-stroke. † With radiator. ‡ Propeller driven at ½ engine speed. § Propeller driven at 900 revs.
Rad. = Radial. Rot. = Rotary. Vert. = Vertical. St.W. = Steel welded. C.B. = Copper brazed joints.
C.E. = Copper electrolytically deposited. C.S. = Copper screwed joint. C.R. = Copper with rubber joints.
F. & T. = Forced to shaft bearings and trough elsewhere. P. = Pump. D.P. = Double pump. F.F. = Fully forced.
W.M. = White metal. R. & P.R. = Rockers and push rods. R. = Rockers. O.R. = Overhead camshaft and rockers.

Notes; *The above particulars were published at the time of the competition. The official report records a total of 56 engines entered originally by 27 companies from which 26 engines arrived at Farnborough. Green's themselves submitted two 100.H.P. engines*

Green 100.H.P. engine C.6.No.30 *used by both Cody and Grahame-White on display in the Science Museum*

equipped their small works at Twickenham with a Heenan and Froude brake for testing engines manufactured elsewhere and for preparing them for delivery.

Green engines found applications in high speed motor boats which may have stemmed from Fred May's interest and was, of course, a convenient means for demonstrating the merits of the engine to potential customers. Defender II, a 21 ft. launch built by Burgoines at Kingston in 1910 achieved 37 knots with a 35 HP Green, an engine later stated to develop 71 HP. In 1913 May was using a five-stepped hydroplane named Pierette with a 60 HP engine to demonstrate on the Thames to E T Willows of airship fame and the "Autocar" magazine representative. The major application, however, came in wartime, when two engines of 250/300 HP were employed in a number of coastal motor boats (C.M.Bs) a purpose for which they were more suitable than for aircraft, their bare weight of 900 lbs. being excessive by that time. The long slender crankshafts of these engines under some conditions, such as misfiring of one or two cylinders, suffered from torsional vibration which could result in fracture.

Throughout the war and into the Twenties Green engines continued to be scaled-up and used in marine applications. The catalogue of 1919 listed various Vee and broad-arrow types, the largest being a 1000 HP 24 cylinder engine with three banks of eight cylinders. These larger engines overcame the need for grouping several small engines and were assembled as a unit with a Green designed reversing gear, used for many years by the Royal Navy. Peter Brotherhood Ltd. manufactured a number of these large engines in a department which continued to be known as the "Green Shop" thereafter.

Despite the success of the Military Competition, Green engines saw little aviation use in wartime, small numbers of the 120/150 HP six cylinder only being used in SS and SSP airships and one each of the prototypes of the FE2a and Avro 523 Pike. They were also used as replacements for the front Sunbeam engine in some of the Coastal (C class) airships of which 28 saw service with the R.N.A.S. Among the applications for the V12 engine rated at 260 HP was as the central pusher engine in the Porte Baby flying boat, ten of which were built, although later it is believed the Greens were replaced by Rolls Royce engines as installed in the outboard positions. The six and twelve cylinder engines for aviation used by the War Office and Admiralty were manufactured against contracts placed with Mirrlees, Bickerton and Day Ltd. of Stockport who produced 42 of the former between September 1914 and April 1917 and 21 of the latter between March 1916 and August 1917, a further 54 on contract being cancelled. However, this was not the end of the story for in 1919, with optimistic plans for civil use, a batch of ten engines of the 35 HP type was produced for the Avro Baby lightplane, this time manufactured by Peter Brotherhood Ltd. at Peterborough.

One of the Aster made engines carried H J (Bert) Hinkler non-stop from Croydon to Turin, a distance of 650 miles, in 9 1/2 hours in May 1920, a considerable achievement for a ten year old design.

The first Green engine to be sold abroad was that fitted to the 1910 Avro Triplane supplied to the Harvard Aeronautical Society. A V Roe was also responsible for the sale abroad of two 35 HP Green engines installed in Avro Baby aircraft

1919 Standard Models of Green Engines					
Type	Cooled	Bore	Stroke	RPM	HP
4 Cyl. Vertical	Water	106	120	1250	35-40
6 Cyl. Vertical	do.	140	152	1250	100-110
6 Cyl. Vertical	do.	142	178	1250	150-170
12 Cyl. V.	do.	142	172	1250	275-300
18 Cyl. W.	do.	142	178	1250	450
24 Cyl. W.	do.	165	204	1250	1000*

* In course of construction

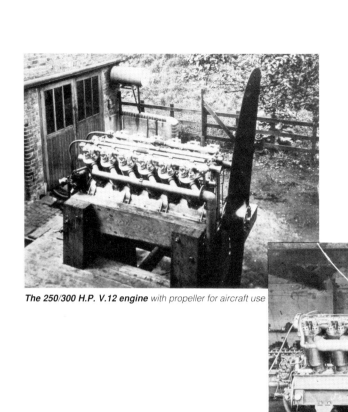

The Green 12,18 and 24 cylinder engines, mainly for marine use

The 250/300 H.P. V.12 engine with propeller for aircraft use

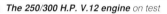

The 250/300 H.P. V.12 engine on test

The 450/500 H.P. W.18 engine for marine use

The 1000 H.P. W.24 engine for marine use. Development was discontinued

exported in 1921-22. One for Russia was flown from Hamble across Europe on its delivery flight by its Russian pilot and the other for India survived there until 1929. In wartime the British Government transferred the non-rigid airships SS.44-47 to Italy and SS. 48-49 to France from the batch of ten Armstrong-Whitworth built ships mostly with Green Engines. SS.40 known as the Black Ship, was operated over the lines under Army control during the summer and autumn of 1916 but returned to this country for further service.

In the post-war years, apart from their use in the Avro Baby, the main usage of Green engines was in marine applications. Brotherhoods continued to produce and in 1920 Peter Hooker Ltd. of Walthamstow were offering a six cylinder 110 HP Hooker-Green running on paraffin. In 1923 Gustavus Green produced a 1 1/2 litre four cylinder marine engine with cast block, a distinct break from the individual copper-jacketed cylinders, and an example of this was installed in Defender II for trials. In the same year he continued to exercise his ingenuity when he took out patents on a streamlined boat of circular section to be constructed of thin steel sheet and braced internally in the manner of bicycle wheels. The boat was fitted with bilge keels and hydroplanes for high speed and balance on the surface, and a design for a light International Racer of the type using the new 1 1/2 litre engine was prepared employing mahogany skins and some wooden internal structure.

Some of the engineering expertise of the Green Engine Co. no doubt stayed with a young man named Murray Jamieson, who was an employee for a time in the years after the war. He became famous later as the engineer in charge of motor racing developments at the Austin Motor Co. in 1933, where a team of both side valve and twin overhead camshaft Austin Sevens was produced and raced for a number of years. Later he worked on the design and development of the E.R.A. until his death in 1938, when he was killed by a runaway car, when a spectator at a Brooklands race meeting.

Gustavus Green gradually retired from business life in the Twenties and the achievements of his engines were surpassed by many other manufacturers and largely forgotten until 1959 when the R.Ae.S. recognised his contribution to early aviation by conferring on him a well-deserved Honorary Companionship, the diploma being presented to him by the President, Sir Arnold Hall, at a ceremony at Hamilton Place. He was then aged 94 and this recognition, coming, as it did, so long after the work for which it was conferred, was some consolation at least in his last years, for he died on the 29th December 1964 within three months of his 100th Birthday, having been able to deal with the intricacies of watch and clock making and repairs as a hobby up till the end.

Several Green engines of the 35, 60 and 100 HP types have survived mostly in Britain, but in the Queensland Museum in Brisbane, Australia Hinkler's engine exists in the Avro Baby in which he made the flight to Turin and which won the Aerial Derby on handicap in 1919 and was second in 1920. This aircraft was also used by him in Australia in 1921 to fly 800 miles non-stop from Sydney to his home in Bundaberg. None of the other survivors listed are installed in aircraft.

Gustavus Green received an Honorary Companionship of the Royal Aeronautical Society in 1959. This picture taken at about that time shows him with the 100 H.P. engine with which Cody won the British Empire Michelin Trophy No.2 in 1912. The engine, C.6.No.30 was used by Grahame-White in his 'Charabanc' subsequent to Cody's death in August 1913 and is on display at the Science Museum

Green Engine Types

Type	Date	Capacity (cc)	Bore/Stroke	Weight (lbs)	Special Features	Remarks
80/100 HP **8 CYLINDER 90° VEE** 82 HP at 1100 RPM	1908-9	11,850	116mm x 140mm		Fluted water jackets	Only one made and used in the Airship Gamma. Priced at £400 in 1910.
30/35 HP C4 **4 CYLINDER IN LINE** (or 44NSG & G4.35 Brotherhood built)	1908	4,158	105mm x 120mm	165	Fluted water jackets. Camshaft vertical drive between Nos. 2 and 3 cylinders.	
30 HP at 1100 RPM 35HP at 1160 RPM 40 HP at 1220 RPM (Not guaranteed for long periods)	1909-10	4,158	105mm x 120mm	158	First engine had magneto driven from top camshaft drive box and water pump from end of crank-shaft. Rotary water pumps changed to gear type later.	Weight was less flywheel 23 1/2 lbs. and ignition 14-19lbs. Fuel consumption 0.6 pints per HP per hour. Overall dimensions: 39"x28"x16". £265 in 1910. £300 in1913.
Alexander Prize Results 31.5 HP at 1213 RPM continuous for 24 hours 36.4 HP at 1390 RPM Max. for 7 mins.	Oct. 1910	4,158	105mm x 120mm	219	Green carburettor	Weight as defined in regulations included 'all parts for the runnig of the engine.
44 HP at 1260 RPM 47.5 HP at 1345 RPM 52.5 HP at 1460 RPM	1911	4,158	105mm x 120mm	184	Extra exhaust ports drilled in Cylinder barrels as tested at Aster Works on RENAUD Brake for J W Dunne.	The weight recorded by 'Flight' in April 1911 was 193lbs with all access. less the radiator & connections
	1919-20	4,158	105mm x 120mm	184	Aluminium pistons & modified camshaft & valve gear.	Brotherhood built engines for Avro Baby.
50/60 HP D.4 (OR 460SG) **4 CYLINDER IN LINE** 50 HP at 1050 RPM 60 HP at 1000 RPM 70 HP at 1200 RPM	1909	8,990	140mmx146mm	250	Rotary Water Pump. Green carburettor.	As exhibited at Paris Show in Sept/Oct. 1909. Stroke quoted by Flight as 140mm probably incorrect. Weight without flywheel (37lbs) or magneto.
50 HP at 1150 RPM	1910	8,990	140mmx146mm	310		Weight quoted with all accessories. Price £365 in 1910. £400 in 1913.
Alexander Prize Results 61.6HP at 1150 RPM 67.8 HP at 1210 RPM for 7 mins.	1911 Dec.	8,990	140mmx146mm	302	Zenith carburettor. Extra exhaust ports drilled in cylinder barrels.	Winner of £1,000 Prize. Contest held at Farnborough.
65 HP at 1250 RPM 72 HP at 1300 RPM	1914	9,385	140mmx152mm	298	Increased stroke.	As listed in 'Flight' 14.3.14 for Olympia Aero Show. Also G A Burls, in 'Aero Engines' (1916 edition).
90/150 HP E.6 (OR 6100G) **6 CYLINDER IN LINE**	1912 Sept.	14,030	140mmx152mm	447	2 Zenith carburettors. Mechanical joints for water connections not hoses. Exhaust valve lifters for starting. Connecting rods drilled for lightness.	Price £750 as shown at Olympia in February 1913.
102 HP continuous 120 HP at 1300 RPM	1914 April	14,030	140mmx152mm	440	With extra exhaust ports. Stiffened crankshaft. Hot air duct to carburettor intakes.	Winning engine in the Naval & Military Aero Engine Competition winning £100 for successfully performing the elementary trial of 6 hrs. continuous running and the final £5000 award.
150 HP	1916				No data available but presumed to be a development of the basic 6 cylinder.	

Type	Date	Capacity (cc)	Bore/Stroke	Weight (lbs)	Special Features	Remarks
250/300 HP **12 CYLINDER 60° VEE**						
250/270 HP	March 1914	30,480	140mmx165mm	900 (with radiator)		As originally reported in 'Flight' prior to Olympia Aero Show.
1200/1300RPM	July 1915	32,700	142mm/172mm	900 (with radiator)	Increased bore and stroke. Crankcase ventilation ducts grouped and reversible for tractor or pusher use. Later engines had 7 mounting brackets on each side of crankcase. 4 Zenith carburettors.	Little aviation use. Mainly used in coastal motorboats (C.M.Bs.) 2 engines of 250 HP or 4 engines giving 1000 HP fitted.

Note: Type numbers appear in two positions on some engines. The oval plate which bears the Green Engine Co. name has type and serial numbers, e.g. C.6 No. 30. Small additional brass plates, where fitted, carry the alternative numbers. The oval plate quoted patent numbers and some later types gave the firing order and specified the use of Mobil Oil or quoted the name of the actual manufacturer.

The 35 H.P. Green in the Royal Scottish Museum. This Aster made engine has the rotary type water pump and the additional oil feeds to the cylinder walls. A deepened oil sump has also been fitted, Type 44 NSG No.726 on the small brass plates, Type C.4 No.23 on the oval plate bearing both Green and Aster Co. names

60 H.P. Green. 460.SG. No.1043W
The Alexander Prize engine of 1911.

With "The most distinguished history of any aero-engine": the 35-H.P. Green in Mr.Hinkler's avro "Baby."

Hinkler's 35 H.P. engine from the Avro Baby in the Queensland Museum

35 H.P. C.4. No.22 (No.823W) in the R.A.F. Museum, Hendon. ▶

◀ *35 H.P. Type 44.NSG. No725.W* rebuilt by the author 1975-77.

26

British Aircraft fitted with Green Engines

Aircraft Type	No. of Seats	Date	Engine HP	Aerodrome or Factory	No. Built with Green	Pilot/Owner	Notes
A.S.L. No. 2 Pusher Monoplane	1	1909	60	Salisbury Plain	1	H Barber Etc.	Built by Howard Wright at Battersea.
A.S.L. Valkyrie Type A Canard Pusher Monoplane	1	9.1910	35	Salisbury Plain	3*	Aeronautical Syndicate Ltd. (A.S.L.)	A.S.L. closed down in early 1912. Valkyrie Monoplanes allocated to Navy at Shorncliffe Camp for experiments in October 1912.
A.S.L. Valkyrie Type C Canard Pusher Monoplane	3	11.1910	60	Hendon	4*		* Not confirmed.
Avro (Roe) Type II Mercury Tractor Triplane	1	1910	35	Manchester/ Brooklands	1	A V Roe	
Avro (Roe) Type III Tractor Triplane	2	1910	35	Manchester/ Brooklands	3	A V Roe. Harvard Aeronautical Soc.	Nos 2 & 3. No. 4 Possibly 2 more built with Green engines. — No. 1 with 35 HP J.A.P. engine and No. 2 burnt on train near Wigan on way from Weybridge to Blackpool Meeting 27.7.10.
Avro (Roe) Type IV Tractor Triplane	1	1910-11	35	Manchester/ Brooklands	1	A V Roe School	
Avro Type D Tractor Biplane	1/2	1911-14	35	Manchester/ Brooklands/Shoreham	4	Various	No. 1 converted to seaplane June 1911. Cmdr. Schwann. Barrow-in-Furness. (No. 2 Circuit of Britain M/C with ENV). Nos. 3 & 4 Avroschool. Engine of No. 4 had additional holes drilled in cylinders for improved scavenging. No. 5 similar to No. 2 but with Green.
Avro Type G (502) Enclosed Cabin Tractor Biplane	2	1912-13	60	Manchester/ Shoreham	1	Parke/Raynham	Flown by Lt. Parke in military trials Aug. 1912. 2nd A/C with A.B.C. not completed. Raynham established duration record (Michelin Prize No.1) 7 hrs. 31 mins. on 24.10.1912 but beaten same day by Hawker with 8 hrs. 23 mins.
Avro 504K Tractor Biplane	2		100	—	-	—	Experimental installation only.
Avro 523A Pike Tractor Biplane	3	8.1916	2x150	Manchester/ Hamble	1	Raynham	First 523 with Sunbeam pusher engines. No production.
Avro 534 Popular/ Baby Tractor Biplane	1	1919	35	Hamble	1	Hamersley	Prototype with pre-war engine crashed on first flight. Unregistered.

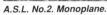
A.S.L. No.2. Monoplane.

A.S.L. Valkyrie Type A.

A.S.L. Valkyrie Type C.

Avro (Roe) Type II Mercury Triplane.

Avro (Roe) Type IV Triplane.

Avro Type D. Hydro-Biplane.

Avro (Roe) Type III Triplane The Boston-Harvard machine.

Avro Type D. Biplane.

Howard Pixton on the *Avro Type D* at Brooklands.

Avro Type G.(502). ▲
▼

Avro 523A. Pike.

Avro 534A. Baby

Avro 534 Popular/ Baby Prototype.

Avro 534A. Water Baby.

Avro 543 Baby 2-seater.

Avro 534 Baby Special with Leigh Venetian Blind Wing.

Aircraft Type	No. of Seats	Date	Engine HP	Aerodrome or Factory	No. Built with Green	Pilot/Owner	Notes
Avro 534 A-D Baby Single Seater	1	1919-22	35	Hamble	8	Hamersley/ Hinkler Etc.	No. 1 K131/GEACQ. Replacement built with engine from prototype. Competed in Aerial Derby June 1919, won Victory Trophy Race in July and then flew Hounslow-Brussels for Aero Show. Hinkler Croydon-Turin 9¹/₂ hrs. on 31.5.20 At Aero Show Olympia July 1920. Hinkler to Australia G-AUCQ flew 800 miles Sydney-Bundaberg 11.4.21. Later VH-UCQ. Preserved Queensland Museum, Brisbane.
Avro 534A Water Baby	1	1919-21					No. 2 G-EAPS. Type 534A. Twin Float Seaplane.
Avro 534B	1	1919-20					No. 3 G-EAUG. Type 534B. Reduced span to lower wing.
Avro 543 Baby 2-seater	2	1920-34					No. 4 G-EAUM. Type 543. 2 Seater later fitted with Cirrus I engine.
Avro 534C	1	1921-24					No. 5 G-EAXL. Type 534C. Further reduced span to lower wing.
Avro 534D	1	1921-29					No. 6 G-EAYM. Type 534D. Tropicalised for use in India.
Avro 534	1	1922					No. 7 G-EBDA. Type 534. Flew London-Moscow by stages on delivery to Russia by pilot Gwaiter.
Avro 534 Baby Special	1	1920					No. 8. Unregistered. Fitted experimental Leigh Venetian Blind Wing.
Bass Paterson Flying Boat	2	1914-15	100	S E Saunders Ltd Cowes I.O.W.	1	E C Bass/ C Paterson	Burnt accidentally before flight.
Blackburn Heavy Type Tractor Monoplane	1	Apr.1909-24.5.10	35	Leeds/Marske	1	R Blackburn	First Blackburn aeroplane built.
Blackburn Type E Tractor Monoplane	1	Apr. 1912-June 1912	60	Leeds/Filey/ Brooklands	1	Indian Aviation Co. (W Lawrence)	First Blackburn type built mainly of steel tube. Excessively heavy. Named "L'oiseau Gris"
Cody Type II A, C&D Pusher Biplane	2	1909-11	60	Farnborough	1	S F Cody	Originally intended to have 2 x 60 HP Green engines but flown initially with one; then 60 HP ENV. The aircraft won Michelin Trophy No. 1 1910 with one Green engine.
Cody Type III Pusher Biplane	2	1910-11	60/80	Farnborough	1	S F Cody	Won Michelin Trophies Nos. 1 & 2, 1911 and Mortimer Singer Prize. Fourth in Circuit of Britain.
Cody Type V.C. Pusher Biplane	2	1912-13	100	Farnborough	1	S F Cody	Won Michelin Cup No. 2 1912. This aircraft and one other supplied to R.F.C. with Austro-Daimler engine. One engine still exists in Science Museum, London.
Cody Type VI (Waterplane) Pusher Biplane.	2	1913	100	Farnborough	1	S F Cody	Flown only as a landplane. The machine in which Cody was killed in August 1913.
Collyer-England Tractor Biplane	1	1912	35	Shoreham	1		Originally built with 50 HP Alvaston engine in 1911.
Dunne D.5 Pusher Biplane	2	1910-11	60	Leysdown	1	J W Dunne	* Single propeller originally. Twin chain-driven propellers later.
Dunne D.6 Pusher Monoplane	1	1911-12	60	Eastchurch	1	J W Dunne	* The Dunne machines were built by Short Bros. For Blair Atholl syndicate.
Dunne D.8 B Pusher Biplane	2	1913	60	Eastchurch	1	J W Dunne/ N S Percival	* Also built with 50 & 80 HP Gnome engines.
Eastbourne Circuit Seaplane Tractor Biplane	3	1914	100	Eastbourne	1	F B Fowler/ Hucks	Twin tractor propellers driven by shafts and bevel gears. Dismantled after Circuit of Britain abandoned.
F.E. 2a Pusher Biplane	2	1.1915	100	Farnborough	1		Underpowered - Replaced by 120 HP Beardmore engine and developed into FE.2b.
Flanders F. 2 Tractor Monoplane	1	8.8.11-10.11	60	Richmond/ Brooklands	1	R C Kemp	Reconstructed to become F.3.

Avro 504K.

Bass Paterson Flying Boat.

Blackburn Heavy Type Monoplane.

Cody Type II C & D. Biplane.

Cody Type IIC. 1910 Michelin No.1 aircraft.

Blackburn Type E. Monoplane.

Cody Type III Biplane. 1911 Circuit of Britain and Michelin Nos.1 and 2 Trophies.

Cody Type VC. Biplane. 1912 Michelin No.2 trophy.

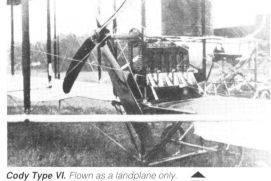

Cody Type VI. Flown as a landplane only.

Cody Type VI. Waterplane.

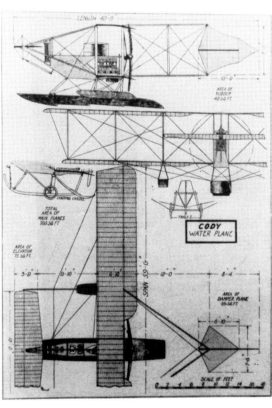

Collyer-England Biplane.

Dunne D.5. Biplane.

Dunne D.8.B. Biplane.

Dunne D.6. Monoplane.

F.E.2.A.

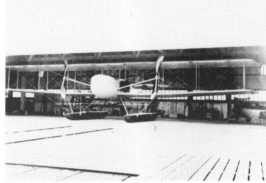

Eastbourne Circuit Seaplane.

Flanders F2. Monoplane.

Flanders F2. Monoplane.

George and Jobling Biplane.

Gnosspelius Hydro-Biplane.   *Grahame-White Type XV.*

Grahame-White Type 10. Charabans.

Handley-Page Type B.(H.P.2)
also known as Planes Ltd. Biplane.

Handley-Page Type D.(H.P4).

Hornstein No.1. Biplane.

Aircraft Type	No. of Seats	Date	Engine HP	Aerodrome or Factory	No. Built with Green	Pilot/Owner	Notes
Flanders F.3 Tractor Monoplane	2	10.1911 13.5.12	60	Richmond/ Brooklands	1	R C Kemp/ E V B Fisher	Crashed killing Fisher and passenger.
George & Jobling Pusher Biplane	1	1910	60	Newcastle/ Gosforth	1	A.E. George	Exhibited at Olympia Show 1910.
Gnosspelius Hydro Tractor Biplane	2	1913	100	Lake Windemere	1	Lt. J F A Trotter	Underpowered.
Grahame-White Type XV Boxkite Pusher Biplane	2	1914	60	Hendon	1	Grahame-White School R.N.A.S.	Developed from Type XII of 1912. Mainly with Gnome engine. Later versions with nacelle and wing extensions.
Grahame-White Charabanc Type 10 Pusher Biplane	5	1913-14	100	Hendon	1	Louis Noel/ R H Carr	Flew with 8 aboard with 120 HP Austro-Daimler. Replaced by Green bought from Cody's effects. Carr won 1913 Michelin Cup No. 1 with engine which still exists in Science Museum.
Handley Page Type B (H.P.2)	1-2	1909-10	60	Barking Freshfield (Liverpool) Formby	1	Planes Ltd R C Fenwick	Later known as Planes Ltd. Biplane when reconstructed.
Handley Page Type D (H.P.4) Tractor Monoplane	1	1910	35	Fairlop	1	R C Fenwick	At Olympia Show 1911. Engine changes to 60 HP Isaacson for Circuit of Britain - crashed before.
Harper Tractor Monoplane	2	1912	60	Paddington	1	A M Harper	Partly built by Weston-Hurlin Co. for the Military Trials.
Hornstein No. 1 Pusher Biplane	1	1909-10	35	Westminster/ Halliford	1	N A Hornstein	Built by Thames Bank Wharf Co. Curtiss type aileron control. Front elevator. Assembled with Green but flown with 35HP J.A.P. at Halliford 25.3.10. No. 2 with 60HP Green not completed.
Humphreys No. 1 Tractor Monoplane	1	1909-10	60	Wivenhoe/ Colchester	1	J Humphreys	Extension shaft drive. 4 wheel under-carriage. Built at Forrestt's Boatyard. At the Bournemouth Meeting.
Humphreys No. 2 Tractor Monoplane "The Elephant"	1-3	1910-11	60	Wivenhoe/ Brooklands	1	J Humphreys G Bell	Originally with extension shaft, later re-moved. Antoinette type under-carriage. Also built at Forrestt's but reconstructed at Brooklands Shed No. 10.
Lamplough Orthopter Biplane	1	1909	50	Willesden	1	Lamplough & Son.	Swaying wings for rising vertically. Incomplete at Olympia Aero Show March 1909. Development discontinued.
Martin-Handasyde No. 3 Monoplane	1	1910-12	35	Brooklands	1	H P Martin/ D G Gilmour	Originally with 65 HP Antoinette and 40.H.P. J.A.P. Green installed temporarily in 1911.
Megone Pusher Biplane	2	1912-14	35 & 60	Hawkinge	1	W B Megone	Extension shaft and chain drive.
Neale 7 Pusher Biplane	1	1.8.1910	35	Brooklands	1	J V Neale/ B Rippin	Wing tip rudders
Northern Aircraft Co. PB 1 Seaplane	2	1916	60	Windemere	1	W R Ding	Modified to PB. 2 with 80 HP Gnome
Poynter Tractor Monoplane	1	1910	60	Battersea/ Brooklands	1	EJ Poynter	Built by Howard Wright
Porte Baby Flying Boat Pusher/Tractor Biplane	5	1916	260	Felixstowe/ Killingholme	10	R.N.A.S.	2 tractor or pusher 250 HP Rolls Royce Eagle1. Central pusher. Green on some a/c. Ultimately 3 - 325 HP Rolls Royce Eagle VII or 360 HP Eagle VIII. Contractor: A/C Manufacturing Co. Hendon. Constructed by subsidiary May, Harden & May, Southampton.
Short/Rolls Powered Glider (R.P.G.)	1	1910	35	Leysdown	1	C S Rolls	Not completed.
Short No. 1 Pusher Biplane	1	1909	30	Battersea/ Leysdown	1	F K McClean	Incomplete at Olympia March 1909 and reported to employ a Green engine. Attempts to fly with 30 HP Nordenfelt and Wright (Barriquand & Marre) engines in Sept. and Oct. 1909 failed. Development using Green not continued.

Humphreys No.1. Monoplane. *Arriving dismantled at the Bournemouth meeting.*

Humphreys No.1. Monoplane.

Humphreys No.2. Monoplane. 'The Elephant'.

Lamplough Orthopter.

Martin-Handasyde No.3. Monoplane.

35 H.P. Green. *Installation in the Neale 7.*

Neale 7. Biplane.

Megone Biplane.

Northern Aircraft Co. PB1. Seaplane.

Poynter Monoplane.

Porte Baby Flying Boat.

Short No.1. Biplane.

Short-Rolls Powered Glider. R.P.G.

Short No.2. Biplane.

Short No.3. Biplane.

Sonoda Biplane.

Sopwith Burgess-Wright.

Sopwith Landplane version of the *Circuit Seaplane.*

Sopwith Bat Boat.

Sopwith Circuit Seaplane.

Aircraft Type	No. of Seats	Date	Engine HP	Aerodrome or Factory	No. Built with Green	Pilot/Owner	Notes
Short No. 2 Pusher Biplane	1	10.1909	60	Leysdown/ Eastchurch	1	Moore-Brabazon	Flew in September with Vivinus engine. Took Daily Mail £1000 prize in October 1909 with Green. Winner of 1909 Michelin Trophy March 1910. Exhibited at Olympia Show March 1910. Launched by rail and derrick.
Short No. 3 Pusher Biplane	1	3.1910	35	Leysdown	1	C S Rolls	Exhibited at Olympia Show March 1910. Unsatisfactory. Dismantled - chassis and engine used in Rolls powered glider. Incomplete July 1910 when Rolls died.
Short S.26 & S.28	1	6.1910	35/60	Eastchurch	2	McClean Moore-Brabazon/ McClean	McClean replaced original Green in S.28 with 50 HP Gnome after purchase. Later fitted 60HP Green for abortive attempt on Baron de Forest Prize. Both S.26 and S.28 reverted to Gnome at end of 1910.
Sonoda Tractor Biplane	2	7.10.1912	60	Hendon	1	C W Meredith	Built by Handley Page Ltd to designs of T Sonoda of Japan.
Sopwith Burgess- Wright	2	5.1912	35	Brooklands	1	Sopwith	Green replaced Gnome briefly before final installation of 40 HP ABC.
Sopwith Bat Boat Amphibian Pusher Biplane	2	1913	100	Kingston/Cowes	1	H G Hawker	Winner of Mortimer Singer Prize for Amphibians 8.7.13. Also fitted with 90 HP Austro-Daimler engine when exhibited at Olympia Show 1913.
Sopwith Circuit Seaplane Tractor Biplane	2	1913	100	Kingston/Hamble	1	H G Hawker/ Raynham	Built for Daily Mail Circuit of Britain 1913. Hawker abandoned first attempt at Yarmouth. Hawker crashed near Dublin on second attempt. Awarded £1000 consolation prize.
Sopwith 2 seater Tractor Biplane	2	1913-14	100	Kingston/Brook- lands/Calshot	1	H G Hawker	Circuit seaplane rebuilt as a land machine. Crashed 8.10.13. Failed Michelin attempt 19.11.13. To Navy Apr. 1914.
Wells Reo Tractor Biplane	1	6.1915	35	Chelsea/Cobnor	1	Wells Aviation Co.	Prototype only.
Wigram Flying Boat	2	1913	100	S E Saunders Ltd Cowes, I.O.W.	1	Wigram Flying Boats Ltd (Arthur Wigram)	Construction abandoned.

Wells Reo Biplane.

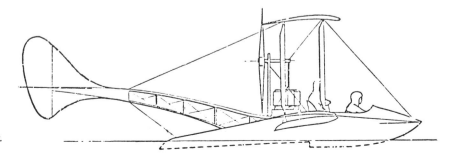

Wigram Flying Boat.

Airships Fitted with Green Engines

Name	Date	Engine HP	Aerodrome or Factory	Capacity Cub.Ft.	Length Ft.	Diam Ft.	Notes
Baby (Dirigible No. 3)	23.11.1909 10.12.1909	35	Farnborough	24,000	81	24	Previously fitted with 2 - 8HP Buchet and with 1 - 25HP R.E.P. First flown 11.5.1909. With Green Nov-Dec 1909.
Beta 1 (Dirigible No.3)	5.1910	35	Farnborough	33,000	104	24	Rebuilt from Baby. Re-engined with 40HP Clerget in 1912.
Gamma (Dirigible No. 2)	12.2.1910-	80	Farnborough	72.000	160	46	Later rebuilt with 2 - 45HP Iris Engines. 1912
Spencer No. 4	5.7.1913	35	Highbury	26,000	88	24	2 Propellers. Advertised Bovril.
Spencer No. 5	1913-14	2 x 60	Highbury	100,000	150	35	Believed not completed.
SS40-47 (Sea Scout Class)	1916	100	Barlow (Nr. Selby) Yorks	70,000	143	30	SS40 built with 85,000 cub.ft. envelope. SS42 rebuilt as SS42a. Built by Armstrong-Whitworth using FK3 fuselage. Prototype SS27 flew with FK3 fuselage with air cooled Renault and 60,000 cub.ft. envelope.
SSP1-6 (Sea Scout Pusher Class)	1916	100	Kingsnorth	70,000	143	30	Single pusher propeller.
C19, C21 and C25 (Coastal Class)	1917-18	100/150	Kingsnorth	170,000	196	52	In service replacement of front 150HP Sunbeam of some ships only. Rear engine 220HP Renault.
Marshall-Fox } Rigid Airship } See under E.N.V.							

British Army Airship 'Baby' Dirigible No.3.

British Army Airship 'Gamma' Dirigible No.2.

British Army Airship 'Beta 1' Dirigible No.3.

Spencer No.4. Airship

Coastal Class Airship.

*S.S. 40. **Non-Rigid. 'The Black Ship'** used on special duties in France with the Army.*

S.S. 41. 'Sea Scout' Non-Rigid.

S.S.P. 'Sea Scout Pusher' Non-Rigid.

Surviving Green Engines

Power	Ref.	Type/No.	Owner/Location	Remarks
35HP	1	C4 No. 22 (no. 823W)	R.A.F. Museum (on display)	Aster made. Ex C Green via Bexhill R.A.F.A. Rebuilt 1964-6
35 HP	2	C4 NO. 23 (44 NSG No. 726W)	Museum of Flight East Fortune, Scotland (on display)	Aster Made. Purchased from Bridlington, Yorkshire in 1921.
35HP	3	44 N5G No. 725W		Rebuilt A E Tagg 1975-7. Aster made.
35HP	4	G4 35 No. 1	R.A.F. Museum (on display)	Ex Fred May boat Defender II. Brotherhood made. Claimed 70HP developed.
35HP	5		Queensland Museum	Installed in Avro Baby. H J HInkler aircraft. Aster made.
60HP	1	460SG No. 758W	Cody family	Cody's engine. Aster made.
60HP	2	460SG No. 1043W	Science Museum	Alexander Prize engine of 1911. Aster made.
60HP	3	D4 No. 24 460 SG	Universal Equipment Ltd. (Cook family)	Ex C Green. Rebuilt 1964-6. Aster made.
100HP	1	C6 No. 30	Science Museum	Ex Cody/Grahame-White Charabanc.
100HP	2	C6 No. 7 (6.100G NO.2615W)	F.A.A. Museum, Yeovilton (on loan from Science Museum)	Ex SS (Sea Scout) airship.

Green engines awaiting delivery to the R.N.A.S. at the Stockport Works of Mirrlees, Bickerton and Day Ltd.

GREEN'S
PATENT BRITISH AERO
ENGINE.
ADOPTED BY H.M. WAR OFFICE.

Our new Catalogue
Sent on Application.

GREEN'S MOTOR PATENTS SYN., LTD.,
55, BERNERS ST., LONDON, W.

Makers for the Patentees:
The Aster Engineering Company, Ltd.

FEBRUARY 26, 1910.

GREEN'S ENGINE

AERO SHOW

We are exhibiting the Patent British Built
GREEN'S AERO ENGINE
.. as adopted by H.M. War Office at ..
OLYMPIA, MARCH 11-19.

THE GREEN'S MOTOR PATENTS SYNDICATE, LTD.,
55b, BERNERS STREET, LONDON, W.
Makers for the Patentees: The Aster Engineering Co., Ltd.

E.H.G.

Part 2   E.N.V. Engines - Le Moteur en 'V'

The original company was formed in 1908 with offices in Sheffield and later at 87 Davies Street, off Oxford Street in London under the name of The London and Parisian Motor Co. to produce engines designed in Britain. Initially, manufacture of engines was carried out in France only but a large proportion of the castings and forgings were supplied from this country. The works were established at 29 Rue St. Germain at Courbevoie in the suburbs of Paris with further premises at 27 Rue Marceau. The chairman of the company was Capt. Laycock, later General Sir John Laycock Bt., who was also part owner of the French factory with Capt. B D Corbet, Managing Director.

From 1908 to 1911 E.N.V. engines were made and used in a variety of aircraft and airships and during this period had a number of successes. During 1911 their use declined, under the pressure of competition, chiefly from the lightweight air cooled rotary engines until, apart from isolated use, the name disappeared from the aviation scene. The final blow came from the failure of the 100HP engine with overhead valves entered for the Naval and Military Aero Engine Contest of 1914 which suffered from fundamental design problems. The company concerned was more fortunate than many in that it had achieved success in other fields, particularly in the manufacture of bevel gears and camshafts and continued in business until 1968, when it finally closed as a result of labour and management problems when its commitments were taken over by other factories of the Eaton, Yale and Towne group into which it had been absorbed in 1964.

The initial project, as exhibited at the Paris Show in December 1908, was a water cooled, eight cylinder side valve engine designed with two banks of cylinders set at 90° in V form - "le moteur

en "V" - and from this the name E.N.V. was derived. At the time in question, 1908-9, flying was making great progress in France but little had happened in England. The French government had placed tariffs on the import of engineering goods into the country and these factors influenced the decision to establish the works initially in France. As aviation progressed in this country during 1909, it was decided that there was sufficient justification to commence manufacture in London as well; the company was retitled "The E.N.V. Motor Syndicate Ltd. and works were established at Hythe Road, Willesden.

The first employee to be taken on in January by the General Manager, Mr W Hukins, when work started in early 1910 at the Willesden works in Hythe Road was a young man, recently returned from New Zealand, named Joe Gascoyne. Originally apprenticed in railway workshops, he had considerable experience with motor car engines and became established as the engine tester and service engineer and later Works Manager, a position from which he retired in 1946. He died in 1972, at the age of 89, after living in retirement in Devonshire with many memories of the pioneers of aviation with whom he came in contact through his activities when tuning and servicing E.N.V. Engines.

Manufacture of improved types of engines got under way in England in the early part of 1910 and by February sufficient progress had been made for Warwick Wright Ltd. to advertise the "all British E.N.V." This company from September 1909 held the joint concession for the sale of French made engines in this country and also acquired the sole selling rights for the London made engines.

The original design of engine, made only in France, was rated at 50/60HP and at 440lbs. was extremely heavy for the power developed,

E.N.V. Type A. *The original engine made in France only. Valve timing could be varied by means of the handwheel protruding from the rear of the crankcase.*

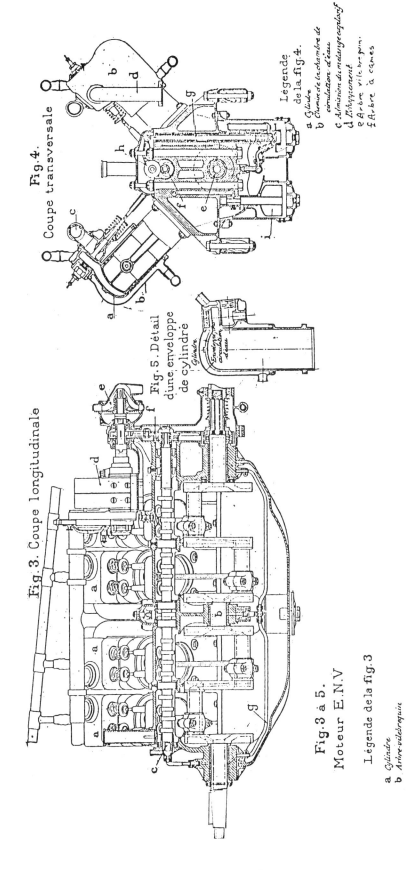

Fig.4.
Coupe transversale

Fig.3 à 5.
Moteur E.N.V

Fig.3. Coupe longitudinale

Fig.5. Détail
d'une enveloppe
de cylindre

E.N.V. Type A 1908.
*The Type C was generally similar but less the control of the valve
operation.*

46

particularly when the additional weight of radiators and coolant was also considered. A cast aluminium crankcase contained the crankshaft which was carried on three large diameter plain bearings. The centre bearing necessitated a wider spacing between the intermediate cylinders than between the others where no bearings were present. The domed pistons were made of steel and operated in cylinders which were of cast iron with domed copper water jackets. These were electrolytically deposited for which process a strong claim of proof against leakage was made. The side inlet and exhaust valves were inside the V of the cylinders and were operated by a central camshaft which was hollow for lubrication. The camshaft was driven by helical tooth gears from the rear of the crankshaft and an additional gear above the camshaft provided the drive for the water pump and magneto.

On this first version of the engine a means was provided for varying the timing of the valves. The control was in the form of a handwheel, mounted at the rear end of the crankshaft, the mechanism being housed in an extension of the casting forming the cover of the gear train. The method of operation is slightly obscure, being variously described in contemporary publications as employing a sliding camshaft or even a sliding crankshaft for varying the lift of the valves. More likely, it would seem to be a sliding adjustment of the gear on the crankshaft. This gear, greater in width than the others in the train and all of sprial tooth form, by its longitudinal movement would cause a change of valve timing and consequently power output. Sliding cams and camshafts controlling valve opening and closing were employed in early petrol engines, more as governors to limit over-speeding, but also as an alternative to throttle control. The inlet ports were on the face of the cylinders inside the V and could be connected to straight inlet pipes along the length of the cylinders to a carburettor at the front. On some engines of this early type distribution was changed by placing the carburettor in the centre of the engine under a spherical mixing chamber from which branches fed the mixture to each cylinder through pipes of almost equal length. This handsome manifold was fabricated from copper sections as a complete unit and could contain a priming tap in the mixing chamber and this feature was carried forward to the later types. The exhaust ports were in the side faces of the cylinders and could be fitted with pipes to carry the exhaust either up or down to suit the particular installation. Duplicated bosses, in the cylinder heads, were provided for the sparking plugs

and for priming cups to assist starting. Dual ignition by battery and coil was an alternative possibility, using a distributor mounted below the water pump driven by an extension of the camshaft. The copper water pipes were joined by short lengths of rubber hose held by wire clips. The heavy weight and the general running difficulties experienced with this early design did nothing to enhance the reputation of the engine.

The identification of this type of engine has not been traced, but for ease of reference it will be retrospectively referred to as Type A. A Type C, which is still in existence, reveals the change made to improve the design by the elimination of the mechanical valve timing control, enabling a simple dog at the rear of the crankshaft to be provided for hand starting. A significant reduction of weight was made by this development, but further improvements were to come later. The report on a test of a Type C engine in June 1909 at the E.N.V. works in Paris by Mervyn O'Gorman, when he was an independant consultant, is on the next page.

In England Joe Gascoyne recalled three of these early types made in France. One of these, believed to be of the first type with sliding camshaft, was fitted to the 1908-9 Voisin biplane "Bird of Passage" brought from France by Moore-Brabazon and exhibited at Olympia in March 1909. The E.N.V. superseded the Antoinette and Belgian Vivinus engines with which he had experience when learning to fly on Voisins at Issy-les-Moulineaux and Chalons and it first flew in England at Eastchurch at the end of April 1909. The Voisin was disposed of to Messrs. George & Jobling, but was little used by Mr George and was later purchased by Cecil Grace but remained at Eastchurch. In March 1910 the "Aero" reported that Moore-Brabazon was purchasing one of each of the "three sizes of E.N.V. engines", however, he in fact ordered a Green engine for his next aircraft - a Short Farman type No. S28 - and as he gave up flying in July for personal reasons following the death of C S Rolls, the optimism of Capt. Hinds-Howell of the Warwick Wright Company for these further sales of E.N.V. engines was not justified. The Green was soon replaced by a Gnome rotary when McClean bought S28 from Moore-Brabazon.

The second French made engine, a Type C, was used by Cody in his 1908-9 aeroplane with which he made his first flights, replacing the Antoinette borrowed from the Aircraft Factory.

Continued on Page 50

REPORT By MR MERVYN O'GORMAN, M.I.E.E., M.I.M.E.

on the

E.N.V. Motor - Type C

SWINBURNE,
O' GORMAN & BAILLIE

82 Victoria Street, Westminster, SW
22nd. June 1909

Report on a Visit to The E.N.V. Works

RUE ST. GERMAIN
COURBEVOIE PARIS

In accordance with your instructions and your letter of the 10th June 1909, I visited the E.N.V. works at 11 o'Clock Saturday morning, the 12th June.

1. Test of Large Engine - I arranged for the immediate testing of the large engine (8 cylinder, 100m/m bore x 130 m/m stroke). The engine was connected to the brake and started its test at 3.30 pm and continued to give 1.3 times its R.A.C. rating at 1,180 RPM for five hours, viz, till 8.30 pm. There was no failure of the engine or of any of its accessories throughout this period, save for one interruption which lasted five minutes and occurred at 7.15 pm. This was due to the petrol tank having run empty unobserved. This stop need not have lasted one minute, but I decided to utilise the occasion to fill the tank completely for the purpose of measuring the petrol consumption during the remainder of the time, viz 1 hour 16 minutes.

2. The Consumption - In 76 minutes was 28 litres (=6 gallons .649 quarts, or approximately 6 gallons 1 1/2 pints) and works out at the rate of .345 litres (.53lbs approximately 8ozs) per horse power hour and shows that the weight of petrol required to be carried by an airship to be propelled for 5 hours by this engine is only 78 kilogs (=approximately 172lbs) or about the weight of one passenger.

This compares favourably with the published results on another engine which gave .357 litres (=.55lbs).

3. The Weight - The weight of the engine, complete with carburettor, all induction pipes, throttle valve, magneto, wires, short exhaust pipes, water pipes and pump, and including a thrust ball-bearing and projecting crankshaft for taking an air propeller direct coupled to the engine was measured and found to be 179.6 kilogs (=359lbs) or at the ratge of 6lbs per HP, as tested for 5 hours. Small residues of oil and water were not extracted from the machine and may be estimated to allow for a deduction of about 1lb from the above weights.

4. Lubrication - The lubrication is entirely by forced circulation, splash being carefully guarded against, and the entire test was run without visible smoke, the necessary extra oil being filled in from time to time through a funnel.

5. Weight of Parts - The weight of cylinders, pistons, connecting rods, base chamber, crankshaft and valves were taken and compared to automobile engines of similar size. The result shows that considerable skill has been exercised in the design and workmanship of the E.N.V. engine, by which substantial weight economies have been secured.

6. General - The engine runs cleanly without appreciable leakage of oil or water. There was a slight misfiring of one cylinder towards end of test for 10 minutes. This was found to be due to a spark plug. The trial was not interrupted and the misfire was cured immediately afterwards.

I am unaware of any independently certified test on an engine of this type and size for flying machines of equal severity or showing equally satisfactory all-round results. It was proposed to run this engine up to 90 HP for 15 minutes by increasing the speed and changing the testing planes of the air brake, but in view of the importance of the test on the smaller engine that was eventually postponed till a later occasion. If 90 BHP can be so obtained, the weight per maximum brake horse power will be under 4 1/2 lbs per BHP and is an excellent result. I took no higher measurements than 65HP but I am in a position to observe that by further opening the throttle and advancing the ignition considerably greater power than 65HP could be obtained from the engine.

(Signed) Mervyn O'Gorman

22nd June 1909

Sole Agents - Jointly
The London & Parisian Motor Company Ltd
87 Davies Street, Oxford Street W
and
Warwick Wright Limited
110 High Street, Marylebone

Voisin of C.A.Moreing with Type A or C engine and gyroscopic stability control above. Pilot. Capt. E.M.Maitland.

Installation of E.N.V. Type C in Moore-Brabazon's Voisin 'Bird of Paradise'.

Continued from Page 47

The third was fitted into a Saunders Hydroplane namesd "E.N.V." kept by "Colonel" Laycock, by which title he was usually known in the works, at 'Thornycrofts' Southampton Boatyard. This installation was successful and "E.N.V." finished fourth in Class 1 at Monaco in 1909. A later 40 HP in a new Saunders hydroplane suffered lubrication problems caused by the small sump and the attitude of the boat at speed, although it did achieve 33 knots in 1910-11.

Work on aeroplanes had been discontinued at the Aircraft Factory at Farnborough by March 1909 but Cody was allowed to keep the aeroplane on which he made the first sustained flight on the 16th October 1908, which had an Antoinette engine which Cody now discarded. The replacement engine he selected for use in the rebuilt aircraft was one of the Type C engines made by the French factory and he flew with this for the first time on the 11th August 1909 and two days later with Col. Capper, the Superintendent of the Factory, as his first passenger. On the 8th September he covered a distance of over 40 miles in 1 hour 6 mins. a short-lived world record at the time.

Noted in "Flight" as being of 80 HP and driving two propellers, the power of the early engines was variously reported as ranging from 50 to 80 HP and running speeds were not always quoted, but these reports were undoubtedly referring to the same basic type of heavy engine made only in France. The methods of testing and equipment for measuring outputs were not entirely reliable and there was a tendency to optimism in advertising the merits of products in the conditions prevailing at the time.

Cody had been experiencing considerable trouble prior to this with his French made engine and his frustration from his failure on having to abandon the Liverpool to Manchester flight caused him to comment adversely on "foreign" engines and to initiate legal action against the company. Joe Gascoyne was sent to Farnborough to investigate, but asked for the engine to be sent to Willesden works for a thorough investigation of the trouble. The substitution of the plugs with Bosch plugs with heavier central electrodes of .050" diameter and heavy earth electrodes to match was Gascoyne's solution of the problem. Cody visited Willesden attired in frock coat and high hat, pulled up his coat tails and sat on a petrol can watching the test run for half an hour and was delighted with the performance. To quote Joe Gascoyne, he said, "Everybody has had a go at that engine Joe, now I shall be able to fly".

Cody required more power for his big machines but made use of his E.N.V. from August 1909 for the rest of the season, until he appeared with his new aircraft which was designed to have two 50 HP Green engines driving one propeller, but, flying with one engine only, he crashed in June 1910. He appeared at the Lanark meeting in August 1910 with his repaired aircraft with the two Greens, which would not synchronise, so he reverted to the old E.N.V. but won no prizes at the meeting. In early November 1910 he fitted a new all British Type F. E.N.V. on loan from the company to the end of the year, with the object of entering the Baron de Forest and other "All British" contests. Various mishaps prevented him competing and by December he had refitted the single Green and with it was able to take the Michelin No. 1 Prize at the end of the month.

Cody was unable to repeat his early achievements of 1909 with the E.N.V., when he had established British Duration and Distance Records and collected a small amount of prize money. He continued with Green engines with considerable success, as already recorded, but was looking for still more power and he was able to acquire cheaply a 120 HP Austro-Daimler engine, available in England from an Etrich biplane crashed by its Austrian Pilot, Lt. Bier, at Hatfield during the 1911 Daily Mail Circuit of Britain Contest. The E.N.V. was discarded thereafter, being among the effects for auction in September 1913 after his unfortunate demise, but remained eventually with the Cody family.

There were a few other French made engines imported before the Willesden works was producing. Among these was, it would seem, a Type A in a Voisin owned by Australian engineer C A Moreing, or by the Australian Electrical Co. of Sydney, with which he was connected. This aircraft was used for trails of a gyroscopic control device at Dagenham from June 1909 and after unsuccessful attempts to fly in the hands of E M Maitland at Doncaster in October, it finally finished its life at Brooklands. The Voisin did not achieve flight and, although Eardley Billing is understood to have used the airframe in the construction of his biplane, there is no evidence of the further use of the old French engine. Moreing is also reported as being connected with an unmanned, radio-controlled airship, which was present at Dagenham in August 1909, said to be powered by a 100/200HP E.N.V. (sic). An E.N.V. engine with this output, the Type T, only became available in June 1911. The airship's engine was a V8 probably of the then current Type C.

The performances of that time seem insignificant by later standards and were soon overshadowed by other feats as aviators competed for the many prizes and trophies put up for competition by various companies and organisations. The engine manufacturers were expected to provide more power for less weight as their contribution to the search for improved performance. The E.N.V. company had developed two new V8 water-cooled engines in the latter part of 1909 which were available initially from the French factory and from April 1910 from Willesden also. These were the Type D of nominally 40 HP and the Type F of 60 HP and were the company's most successful designs although they only appear to have retained their popularity, according to the reports of the time, for a period of about two years. The engine types evolved from the Type C were considerably redesigned with crankshaft main bearings, now consisting of six ball races permitting equal spacing of the cylinders. A double race in the nose of the one-piece crankcase was provided to take either tractor or pusher propeller thrust. The old variable valve timing arrangement had been previously discarded on the Type C and normal throttle control was provided of the Zenith carburettor usually fitted, although White & Poppe units were fitted by some users.

On the smaller engine the carburettor was positioned at the front of the V, the intake manifold being different from the Type F, which continued to use one based on the earlier design with spherical central chamber.

A deep oil sump was fitted to ensure collection of oil in all flight conditions and lubrication of the front bearings was made internally. The cylinder heads and water jackets were now flatter and the valves, which were at a slight angle to the centre line of the cylinders, were operated by way of hardened steel balls, between the camshaft and tappet rods. The gear train driving the camshaft and accessories now used straight spur gears instead of the earlier helical tooth type.

Other improvements included an ignition distributor drive at the rear end of the camshaft, thus removing this from the magneto, or enabling dual ignition by coil. Savings of weight and bulk were achieved with improved power output for the Type F over the earlier engine of slightly larger capacity.

The 1910 season saw a considerable increase in aviation activities particularly in the use of E.N.V. engines of Types D and F mainly the latter. At the Bournemouth meeting, where C S Rolls was killed, as many as 6 competitors were using E.N.V. and this increase in activity was carried on to about the end of the year culminating in the Baron de Forest contest.

Perhaps the greatest achievement using an E.N.V. engine was that of T. O. M. Sopwith in winning the Baron de Forest prize in December 1910 for flying from Eastchurch, a distance assessed as 169 miles, to Beaumont south of Charleroi in Belgium. The prize was for competition by all-British aircraft and Sopwith flew a Howard Wright pusher biplane, a type which used E.N.V. Type F engines almost exclusively and similar aircraft were also used by a number of other competitors. A total of 11 competitors entered aircraft of which nine were to be fitted with the E.N.V. Type F, Cody was to use his Green engined biplane and Ogilvie a Short Wright with N.E.C. engine. Lieut. Watkins was to fly a radio equipped Howard Wright entered by Capt. Maitland, but he damaged this at Shorncliffe before competing. Robert Loraine's Bristol Boxkite with E.N.V. was damaged in its shed during a gale at Swingate Down, Dover, as also was Greswell's E.N.V. engined Grahame-White Farman type machine. Loraine acquired, urgently, a Howard Wright and Grahame-White a Bristil Boxkite as replacement machines, both fitted with E.N.V. but Loraine's machine crashed at Eastchurch and Grahame-White's second Boxkite was destroyed by fire in its hangar at Swingate, caused by a watchman's hurricane lamp, before they could compete.

Born of Irish parentage in Chile, Cecil Grace had started to fly early in 1910 at Eastchurch on the old E.N.V. powered Voisin "Bird of Passage", which he had acquired from George & Jobling and during the following season he flew a variety of aircraft. The types included Short Wright with Green engine, Blériot and Farman with Gnome and later in the season he flew a Short S27 pusher biplane with E.N.V. (C S Grace No. 2). He was a daring and enthusiastic pilot and became well known and admired during the course of the year. In December he decided to make his attempt for the Baron de Forest prize and flew from Eastchurch to Dover for the purpose. On the 22nd Joe Gascoyne started his engine and wished him luck, but when he reached France the weather was misty so he landed near Boulogne and in the afternoon decided to return to Dover, prior to another attempt. Harry Harper, the well known writer, received the news of Grace's departure and Joe Gascoyne took him in Colonel Laycock's 1899 Mercedes to await Grace's return. They finally returned to their hotel at 3am the next morning. The lightship at the Goodwin Sands reported hearing his engine but there was no sign of Grace and it must be concluded that he lost his way in the mist and disappeared in the sea, his cap and goggles being washed up a few weeks later on a beach near Ostend. The need to use an all-British aircraft for this flight had required a change from the French-made engine fitted to Short S27 and Grace eventually used the later aircraft, Works No. S29 (C S Grace No. 3) with top plane extensions and fitted with a British made Type F engine for the de Forest flight.

This French E.N.V. engine still survives and is currently fitted to the replica Short S29 built by Cole Palen and now at Old Rhinebeck, New York. This replica first flew in 1973 and was briefly demonstrated at his air shows held in the summer months but is currently consigned to the museum.

Cecil Grace and his brother Percy had commissioned the reconstruction of the Short S27 as a tractor biplane using an E.N.V. engine. This machine, referred to by the "Aero" as the Short-Grace, but presumably the original Short S32 was brought out at Eastchurch on Saturday 12th November but did not fly, although a week later it was reported to have flown with a mechanic as passenger. It appeared again on Sunday the 27th November but again did not fly due to foreign object damage to the propeller. It seems that this was the last occasion before he was lost that Cecil Grace attempted to use this machine which was intended as his entry in the Baron de Forest contest, for which event, as already recorded, he used the S29 with a British made E.N.V. After Cecil disappeared, work on the tractor aircraft was discontinued, until Frank McClean became interested. It was completed for him late in 1911 with a 70HP Gnome engine as S36 and first flew on 10th January 1912. It became known as the Tandem Tractor and identified T5 on passing to the Admiralty. The actual airframe of S27 was itself used in the construction of the Tandem Twin S27 which was acquired by McClean and first flown by him on 29th October 1911. It remained McClean's property but was loaned to the Admiralty and was finally crashed by Lieut. Samson and written off.

In France, Voisin had used the original heavy type engine in his pusher biplanes and later the Type F also. Bleriot used the Type D and later the Type F in his Type XII monoplane with underslung engine with chain-driven propeller above, which acquired a bad reputation for poor flying characteristics, the first of which crashed and was burnt at the Rheims meeting in August 1910. He may also have used in this type a variant with an extended crankcase and crankshaft known as the Type FA.

Grahame-White purchased the second Blériot XII which he named "White Eagle" and acquired his first piloting experience with it at Issy-les-Moulineaux in November 1909 and later at Pau in Southern France. The poor flying qualities of the type and the damage to man and machine caused him to transfer to the Type XI and the larger machine remained in France until June 1910, when it was donated to the War Office by the Duke of Westminster and Col. Laycock who had purchased it from Grahame-White. By October it was ready to be flown on test by Lt. R A Cammell at Larkhill, which were the first flights made by a British military aeroplane, a first for E.N.V. Despite several unsatisfactory flights, a cross-country delivery flight to Farnborough was begun on the 29th November, during the course of which the Blériot forced-landed. The resulting wreckage was sent to Farnborough to be "reconstructed" and to emerge in the summer of 1911 as the S.E.1 a pusher aircraft of original design, which flew satisfactorily in the hands of G de Havilland but was crashed catastrophically on the 18th August 1911, resulting in the death of Lt. T Ridge, the deputy superintendent of the Aircraft Factory.

Subsequent to its use in the SE1, the E.N.V. engine originally used in the Blériot XII (Type F series 1 no. 13) was fitted to the BE2 Serial No. 205 (originally BE5) for a brief period, but by the autumn it was removed and replaced by a Renault.

A number of lesser manufacturers in France made use of E.N.V. engines, generally the 60 HP type. Leading pilots of the time such as Rougier, De Caters, Duray, Metrot and others took considerable amounts of prize money using E.N.V. engined Voisins at the major continental meetings of 1909 and particularly at the Heliopolis meeting of 1910 when E.N.V. engines took 145,000 francs of the total of 187,000 francs available.

A Voisin purchased by Ehrlich Weiss, Houdini the escapologist, became the first to fly successfully in Australia in March 1910 powered by a 60 HP E.N.V. Apart from Voisin and Blériot machines, a number of other aircraft types of continental origin were fitted with E.N.V. engines in small numbers. In France these included Farman, Antoinette, de Pischoff, Goupy, Fernandez, Guyot et Verdier, Hanriot, Turcat-Mery-Rougier and Savary. The Dufaux borthers of Geneva, makers of Motosacoche motorcycles and the Polish Tanski-Cywinski-Zbieranski biplanes both used E.N.V. engines in 1910-11.

Further afield in Australia a 40 HP E.N.V. powered an autogyro type machine constructed by A J Fortescue of Arnfield, Sydney for which patents were taken out in 1909. This machine was tested in 1910-11 and is reported to have lifted, off the ground, giving sufficient encouragement to proceed with two further machines in 1920-24 but then fitted with Anzani engines. Fortescue claimed his machine to be the "World's First Successful Gyro Plane" and contested, until his death in 1936, the more widely accepted claim of Cierva to this title.

No doubt the Type D and particularly the Type F, E.N.V.'s gave good service to a number of the pioneer flyers and useful work was carried out in Great Britain and abroad, much of which is unrecorded. Sopwith found it very reliable and took his Howard Wright to America in 1911 and used it together with a Bleriot and a Burgess Wright in a successful tour in which he collected a large amount of prize money, which helped with the formation of the Sopwith Aviation Co. after his return.

The Type F engine merited the issue of a Royal Aero Club Certificate of Performance published in the Official Notices to Members on the 18th March 1911, which read as follows:-

---

The Royal Aero Club
Certificate of Performance of an E.N.V. 8-Cylinder Motor

Wednesday March 8th 1911

Fitted with high-tension magneto and coil and battery ignition. Water for cooling supplied from auxillary tank, circulation induced by pump on motor.

Petrol: Shell from gravity-fed tank.

Engine started 12 H 7M 30S pm developing 60 brake horse-power. Engine stopped at 12.46pm and re-started 12.47pm.

Cause of stop: Obstruction in petrol pipe from tank to carburettor.

At 2.16pm the engine ran somewhat irregularly, the brake horse-power dropping to 56. At 2.25pm revolutions were regained and 60 brake horse-power indicated. From 2.27pm to the end of the run the engine developed 66 brake horse-power. The engine was stopped at 3H 8M 30S pm. With the exceptions noted above the engine developed 60 horse-power throughout the run.
At 3H 11M 30Spm the engine was again started without any adjustments having been made and developed 66 horse-power within a few seconds.

A K Huntington
Major F Lindsay-Lloyd Technical Committee

Harold E Perrin, Secretary
166 Piccadilly, London W   March 9th 1911

Note: The horse-power was tested by a Walker's fan dynamometer and Elliott's speed indicator, the horse-powers stated being those shown on the diagram supplied by the makers of the dynamometer for the speed of the engine and position of the fan blades.

A further test observed by the R.A.C. of a two hour non-stop run was carried out on the 2nd August 1911 and subsequently another Certificate of Performance was issued of which the following is an extract:

"Period. The engine was started at 4hrs. 4 mins. 10 secs. running at 1130 rpm. At 4 hrs. 6 mins. 20 secs. the throttle was shut down to give 1120 rpm At 4 hrs. 32 mins. 35 secs., the revs. stood at 1140 rpm which speed remained constant throughout the run. At 6 hrs. 4 mins. 10 secs. the throttle was shut down, the engine having been run for 2 hours. At 6 hrs. 5 mins. 0 secs. it was opened and the speed accelerated to 1200 rpm. the engine running at this speed till 6 hours 6 mins. 50 sec.s when the run was brought to a finish at the observer's request.

Performance: By the power chart of the Walker's dynamometer it is shown that the engine developed over 60 HP throughout the two hours' non-stop run, the actual BHP being as follows:

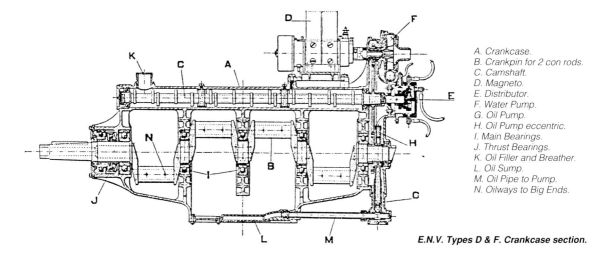

A. Crankcase.
B. Crankpin for 2 con rods.
C. Camshaft.
D. Magneto.
E. Distributor.
F. Water Pump.
G. Oil Pump.
H. Oil Pump eccentric.
I. Main Bearings.
J. Thrust Bearings.
K. Oil Filler and Breather.
L. Oil Sump.
M. Oil Pipe to Pump.
N. Oilways to Big Ends.

E.N.V. Types D & F. Crankcase section.

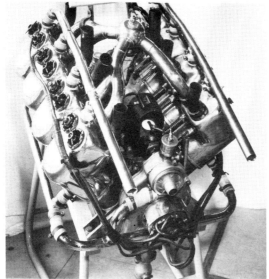

British made E.N.V. Type F No.III
at the London Science Museum.

French made Type F. Series I No.4. *Rebuilt by the author in 1964-5 and later fitted to replica Short S.27/29 by Cole Palen.*

Installation of Type D in Howard Wright Monoplane
flown at Brooklands in 1910 by Capt. Hinds-Howell.

French made Type F.A. Series 3. No.6 *at the Musee de l'Air.*

At 1140 rpm 64.3 BHP At 1200 rpm 75.2 BHP

Remarks: The engine ran very satisfactorily throughout the test.

A K Huntington   Technical Committee
H Waymouth Prance   Observer on behalf of
the Royal Aero Club

Harold E Perrin, Secretary"

These tests show the steady rather than spectacular development of performance and reliability that was typical of the period, with the hope of encouraging potential purchasers to adopt the E.N.V. rather than its competitors' engines.

The second competition for the Alexander Prize for £1,000 in October 1911 attracted entries from seven engine manufacturers including the E.N.V. Motor Syndicate with the Type F. Engines for test had to be delivered to the N.P.L. at Teddington by the end of September. The actual trials were held at Farnborough under N.P.L. supervision, no doubt as a result of complaints from the people at Teddington living near to the N.P.L. about the noise of open exhausts running for long periods during the trials in the previous year. Joe Gascoyne was sent, on behalf of E.N.V. to operate their entry to which some changes had been made. New pistons with an extra ring and a deeper sump and increased capacity oil pump were introduced and a White and Poppe carburettor fitted to a new manifold which omitted the spherical mixing chamber. The requirement was for two runs of 12 hours with no break of more than 10 minutes thus permitting only minor rectifications to be carried out. On the first day the engine was started at 8am and ran till 4pm when a broken water pump coupling was changed in the allowable time, so running continued successfully until 8.10pm that night. The following morning a start was again at 8am but a stop was almost immediately required to reset the brake which had been incorrectly set by an inexperienced N.P.L. man. The resulting overloading may have been the cause of the breakage of a cylinder which, after only 25 minutes, was seen through the windows of the test cell to be wobbling. In this way, success eluded E.N.V. and the prize was finally awarded to the Green Engine Company. Nevertheless, the E.N.V. had produced a consistent 72 HP on the rcorded and earned the praise of F M Green , the chief engineer of the Factory at Farnborough.

E.N.V. deviated from the course that their name implied, by the introduction of a horizontally opposed four cylinder engine shown in Paris in October 1909. This was described as having steel cylinders machined from the solid and with a combined inlet and exhaust valve in each cylinder head. The weight at 30 kgs (66lbs) for 24HP claimed was a good power to weight ratio but perhaps the engine was too weak and no production ensued. In March 1910 a four cylinder engine with integral radiator, identified as Type H, was at the Olympia Show and Warwick Wright issued a catalogue with a few details but no photograph and there were only brief reports in the technical press, some of which conflicted in detail. The Type H was of smaller capacity than the 1909 engine and so provided a small engine in the new range which did not encroach on the field of the Type D. The method of valve operation has not been identified although it was almost certainly OHV and probably similar to the earlier engine.

However, the four cylinger engine again appeared at the Paris Show in October 1910 and was described in the 'Aero' probably by C G Grey as 'a new engine'. It had an integral radiator and weighed 60 kgs (132lbs) for a claimed 30HP. Separate exhaust valve above and inlet valve below the cylinders were used, apparently positively operated by push/pull rods and rocking levers. Ball races were employed for big end and main bearings.

There may well have been balancing or other mechanical problems with the horizontally opposed types to limit their use and there is no evidence of use in 1911 of this type. The only known use of the four cylinder E.N.V. was a Type H in the Neale 6 monoplane in 1910 at Brooklands, where Neale transferred his activities after a period at Dagenham in 1909 with his earlier J.A.P. powered aircraft.

The later V8 engines were also unsuccessful, the first being the Type T which was exhibited at both Aero shows, Paris in 1910 and Olympia in 1911, and was tested but never flown.

The Type T was a large, heavy engine, designed for continuous running at a moderate speed and perhaps more suited for airship use, although it was intended to test it in an Antoinette, but this never happened. It differed in many ways from the earlier V8's although it had some features in common with the four cylinder engine. Steel cylinders replaced the cast iron ones, with which some breakages had occurred, no doubt due to defective castings, when under extreme load. The valves were overhead, positioned vertically, and operated by light pull rods through triangular shaped rockers. The crankshaft was extended forward, as was the crankcase, to accommodate

Rebuild of Type F. Series 1. No.4.
In 1965-6. Originally flown in Short S.27. by Cecil Grace.

On display S.B.A.C. show. Farnborough 1966.

Running again in July 1966 after 52 years in store.
Left to right. Mr. H.Biles of E.N.V. Co, the author and Lieut. Cmdr.
W.J.Tuck of the Science Museum.

large diameter main and thrust bearings, positioning the propeller well forward in a similar manner to the earlier Type FA. The White & Poppe carburettor was mounted at the front on a central pipe extending to the back of the engine where it divided, doubling back on each side to connections at each cylinder. Dual ignition by coil and magneto was provided.

The final E.N.V. engine, attributed to a designer named Mr Rath who may have been responsible for some of the earlier types also, appeared in 1914 and was entered for the Naval and Military Aero Engine Competition starting at Farnborough in May 1914., This was an engine of half the capacity of the Type T with a faster running crankshaft geared to a separate propeller shaft running at 900 rpm. It had overhead valves now set horizontally in the cylinder heads and operated direct through short push rods by a camshaft raised on pillars in the centre of the Vee. The method of retaining the cylinders was novel, consisting of a collar screwing onto the lower end of each cylinder, which carried gear teeth. This was engaged by a small bevel gear on a shaft mounted in the crankcase and was operated by a key outside the crankcase at each cylinder position. This design, while ingenious, did not give positive locking due to clearances and side thrust from the bevels and enabled the cylinders to loosen. Also the high mounting of the camshaft was a source of vibration which played havoc with the operation of the valves. Weight saving had led to generally light construction with tubular connecting rods and a split crankcase with the lower fabricated portion held up by straps, the upper portion a casting forming the main structure, was provided with two mounting bosses, cast-in, through which tubes, passing across the airframe, formed the mounting. A centrifugal pump was driven from the front of the crankshaft to feed coolant to the radiator which was provided as a unit fixed to the engine. The camshaft drove, at its forward end, a distribution valve for a compressed air starter; the rear end was driven by a vertical shaft by bevel gears from the crankshaft, the vertical shaft also driving the plunger type oil pump.

The company had invested heavily in gear cutting equipment, particularly for cutting bevel gears, and camshaft grinders andwhen the engine failed, as it did at an early stage of the Farnborough trials, it left the company with no engine to produce but well placed to specialise in the field of gear manufacture, also for camshafts, for the production of which the company gained a well earned reputation. In wartime the company contributed camshafts and gears to engines made by the Royal Aircraft Factory (R.A.F.) to the Siddeley Puma, Austro-Daimler/Beardmore, B.H.P. Liberty and Ricardo tank engines among others and post-war provided many complete gear boxes to the automobile industry.

A limited amount of use was made of E.N.V. engines in non-rigid airships. The American Walter Wellman, after two unsuccessful attempts to fly to the North Pole, constructed a new 345,000 cubic ft. airship named America, which was fitted with two engines, one a 75 HP Lorraine Dietrich, the other a 60 HP E.N.V. Type F. The airship, which departed from Atlantic City on the 15th October 1910, carried a crew of six and was trailing a floating device called an "equilibrator" intended to regulate the height at which the ship flew and containing additional supplies of fuel. The E.N.V. overheated badly early in the flight and had to be shut down. After 69 hours the airship descended at latitude 35° 43' longitude 68° 18' where the crew were saved by the steamer Trent. The America was seen again floating on the sea on December 9th but was not recovered.

Ernest Willows, a native of Cardiff, started building airships in 1905 and constructed a total of five; his No. 3 named "City of Cardiff" being the most successful. In 1913 he constructed No. 5 at Hendon, a 50,000 cubic ft. non rigid fitted with a 60 HP E.N.V. Type F, which flew for the first time in November. It was used mainly for demonstrations and passenger flights in the locality of Hendon although on one occasion it flew over the centre of London. It finally came to grief in March 1914 after being damaged in its shed during a gale and Willows was forced to deflate it.

In Russia, two non-rigid airships were built in 1910 to be powered by Type F engines, four of which were supplied from the Willesden factory. The first of these was the JASTREB made by the Duks Company, a ship of 2,700 cubic metres capacity; the second was the 'GOLUB' made by Izorsky Zav and of 2,275 cubic metres. Details of their operations are not known and the preparations for Joe Gascoyne to go to Russia to service the engines were not proceeded with.

Two Type F engines were to be supplied in the latter part of 1914 to a syndicate headed by Admiral Fox (retired) who had a scheme to build a rigid airship with rapid climbing ability for countering the Zeppelins. This was sponsored by an American journalist, T R MacMechan of Baltimore, and designed by W R Kamp of New York and was to be built for the Admiralty at Barking by the Marshall-Fox Co. One of the many features for which advantages were claimed was the non-stretch wire cable to drive two propellers mounted outboard on either side of the hull. An E.N.V. then rated at 75 HP was combined with a 125 HP Green to provide the power. The structure was mainly of wood and in November 1915 construction was proceeding but on test at Barking, with naval representatives present, considerable take-up of the jockey pulley, through stretch of the wire cable, was observed. This shortcoming and perhaps misgivings on some of the other novel features caused the Admiralty to lose interest and the airship, although well advanced in construction, was not completed. The Marshall-Fox Co., was reformed as the Fox Super Airship Construction Co. in mid 1916 but nothing further was heard of their airships.

E.N.V. Type D. Installed in a Blériot XI.
Used at the Grahame-White School at Hendon in 1911.

The horizontally opposed four cylinder engine of 1910.

The 100H.P. Type T of 1910

E.N.V. Engine Types

Type	Date	Capacity (cc)	Bore/Stroke	Weight (lbs)	Special Features	Remarks
50HP TYPE A (SV) **8 CYLINDER 90° VEE** 50 HP at 10000 RPM 60.5 HP Max.	1908	8,171	100mm x 130mm	440	Variable lift inlet valves by sliding 'camshaft'. Plain bearings to crankshaft. Wide space between intermediate cylinders to accommodate centre bearing. Exhaust port in side faces of cylinders. External oil feed to front bearings.	French made only. Exhibited Paris Show 1908 and Olympia Show March 1909. Believed used by Moore-Brabazon in Voisin "Bird of Passage".
80 HP TYPE C (SV) **8 CYLINDER 90° VEE** 65 HP at 1180 RPM 90 HP for 15 mins. claimed.	1908-9	8,171	100mm x 130 mm	375	Sliding 'camshaft' and operating gear deleted. Normal throttle control at carburettor	French made only. Used by Cody with some success. (Price 10,000 francs)
35/40 HP TYPE D (SV) **8 CYLINDER 90° VEE** 29.5 HP at 1000 RPM 37 HP at 1250 RPM 40 HP at 1400 RPM	1909-10	4,087	85mm x 90 mm	155	Ball race main bearings. Equal spacing of cylinders. Conventional side valve with ports side by side.	French and British made. £350 in 1910. (7,500 francs)
60/80 HP TYPE F (SV) **8 CYLINDER 90° VEE** 59 HP at 1000 RPM 74 HP at 1250 RPM 88 HP at 1500 RPM	1909-11	7,623	105mm x 110 mm	287	As Type D. Both Zenith and White & Poppe carburettors used. Corrugated brass oil cooler added to sump. Late 1910.	French and British made. £450 in 1910. (10,000 francs)
60/80 HP TYPE FA (SV)	1910				As Type F but with extended crankshaft and crankcase.	French made, used by Bleriot in Type XII.
25/30 HP **4 CYLINDER** **HOR. OPPOSED (O.H.V.)** 24 HP at 1200 RPM	1909 Oct.	4,100	109mm x 110 mm	66 lbs (30kgs)	Steel cylinders machined from solid. Combined inlet and exhaust valve.	French made. 4000 Francs in 1909. Data from "Flight". At Paris Show.
25 HP TYPE H **4 CYLINDER** **HOR. OPPOSED (O.H.V.)** 30 HP at 1200 RPM	1910 Mar.	2,300	90 mm x 90 mm	Under 110lbs (88lbs basic engine)	Weight included integral radiator and coolant. (Warwick Wright catalogue)	"Flight" recorded bore as 85mm was probably incorrect. £175 from Warwick Wright Ltd. At Olympia Show 3,500 Francs.
30 HP UNIDENTIFIED **4 CYLINDER** **HOR. OPPOSED (O.H.V.)**	1910 Oct.	3,050	80 mm x 120 mm	132 lbs (60kgs)	Exhaust valve above, inlet valve below cylinder, positively operated by push/pull rods and rocking levers. Ball races for main and big end bearings. Separate steel cylinder barrel and head machined from solid screwed and brazed together.	Increased stroke unconfirmed. At Paris Show.
100HP TYPE T (O.H.V.) **8 CYLINDER 90° VEE** 100 HP at 1000 RPM	1910-11	15,934	130mm x 150mm	525	Valves positioned vertically operated by light pull-rods and triangular rockers. Dual ignition by coil and magneto. White & Poppe carburettor at front on central pipe extending back and dividing, doubling back each side. Extended crankshaft and crankcase with 10" dia. ball race main bearings. Steel cylinders with copper water jackets.	At Paris Show Oct. 1910 and Olympia in March 1911. £900. Designed for continuous running in both aeroplanes & dirigibles. Tested but not flown.

Type	Date	Capacity (cc)	Bore/Stroke	Weight (lbs)	Special Features	Remarks
100 HP UNIDENTIFIED (OHV)8 CYLINDER 90* VEE 100 HP at 1620 RPM	1914	7,494	95mm x 165mm	450 (with rad.)	Reduction gear 1.8 to 1 to drive propeller at 900 RPM. Cylinders retained by bevel gear type locking. Valves positioned horizontally & operated through short pushrods by camshaft mounted on pillars in centre of Vee and driven by vertical shaft from crankshaft by bevel gearing. Provision for compressed air starting. Radiator provided with engine.	British made. Entered for Naval & Military Aero Engine Competition Farnborough 1914 but withdrawn at an early stage of the trials.

S.F.Cody's surviving engine. A French-made Type C. Series 1. No.3. The wide spacing of Nos.2 & 3 cylinders to provide for the long plain main bearing of this early type E.N.V. engine is apparent.

Cross sectional elevation of the 100 h.p. E.N.V. engine.

Longitudinal sectional elevation of the 100 h.p. E.N.V. engine.

The unsuccessful 100 H.P. E.N.V. engine of 1914.

61

British Aircraft fitted with E.N.V. Engines

Aircraft Type	Date	E.N.V. Type	Aerodrome or Factory	Pilot/Owner	Remarks
Avro Type D Tractor Biplane	1911	F	Brooklands	R Kemp	Crashed at start of July 1911 Circuit of Britain.
Avro Type E Tractor Biplane	3.3.1912-29.6.1913	F	Brooklands/ Shoreham	Avro School	Predecessor of Avro Type 500 with Gnome engine. Crashed at Shoreham 29.6.13. Pilot R N Wight fatally injured.
Avro (Duigan Type) Tractor Biplane	9.1911-10.1912	D	Brooklands	John R Duigan	Small single seater, similar to Type E which it preceded.
B.E.2 Tractor Biplane	1912	F	Farnborough	Royal Aircraft Factory	No. 205 only BE2 fitted with E.N.V. experimentally.
Eardley Billing Tractor Biplane	1911	D	Brooklands	N S Percival	Constructed from C A Moreing's Voisin.
Bristol Boxkite Pusher Biplane	1910	F	Larkhill/Dover Brooklands/Dover	Bristol Co.	Works No. 8 at Lanark meeting Aug. 1910 (Flight 13.8.10 flown by Edmond & Champel. Loraine due to fly in Baron de Forest contest but damaged before competing. Most Boxkites fitted with Gnome engines. Works No. 16.17 Manville Prize 1911 Pixton. Grahame-White due to fly in Baron de Forest contest but damaged twice and was replaced by No. 17 which was destroyed by fire before competing.
Bristol Challenger -England Tractor Biplane	1911-19.5.1912	F	Larkhill	G England/ Bristol Co.	Works No. 59
Cody IC Pusher Biplane	Aug. 1909-Dec. 1909	C	Farnborough	S F Cody	Extensively modified from British Army aeroplane No. 1. Originally with Antoinette engine. Flew for 1hr. 6m. on 8.9.09 over Laffans Plain. Used at Doncaster meeting in October. After unsuccessful attempts to win the Hartley prize for a flight from Liverpool to Manchester this machine was dismantled.
Cody IIB Pusher Biplane	Aug. 1910-Nov. 1910	C and F	Farnborough	S F Cody	Flown initially with one Green engine. 2 Green engines fitted at Lanark would not synchronise. Replaced by French E.N.V. Type C with single propeller at Lanark. Green refitted for Michelin attempt on 4th November. British E.N.V. Type F fitted between 5th-11th November with intention of entering the Baron de Forest contest. Green refitted subsequently and used for Michelin attempts ending in success on 31st December.
Fritz Tractor Monoplane	1910	D		Oyler Co.	Constructed by Oyler & Co. London
Grahame-White Pusher Biplane	1910	F	Hendon	Greswell	Entered for Baron de Forest Prize. Damaged in shed at Dover and withdrawn. Farman type.
Howard Wright Tractor Monoplane	1910	D	Brooklands	Sopwith, Hinds-Howell, Spottiswoode	Modified Avis.
Howard Wright Pusher Biplane	1910	F	Brooklands etc.	Sopwith/Watkins & others	Several built at Battersea Works. On 18.12.10 Sopwith won Baron de Forest prize and briefly held British Distance & Duration Records of 150 miles and 4 hrs. 7 mins. 17 secs., on 31.12.10. Used successfully in America in 1911. Sopwith used White & Poppe carburettor.
Lane Tractor Monoplane	1910	D	London/ Brooklands	Lanes British Aeroplanes Ltd/ C Lane	Also used on floats at Shoreham
Molesworth Tractor Triplane	Aug. 1910	D		H B Molesworth	Rebuild of Mackenzie-Hughes Britannia Triplane.
Mulliner 2 Knyplane Tractor Monoplane	1911	F	Clapham Junction	Mulliner Co.	Exhibited at Olympia Show
Neale 6 Tractor Monoplane	1909	H	Brooklands	J Neale	Later fitted with 20 HP J.A.P.
Percival Parseval 1 Tractor Biplane	1912 Jan.-Sept.	F	Brooklands	N.S. Percival Aero Construction Co.	2 seater based on the Eardley Billing used for instruction. Eventually used for flight testing the Adams-Dorman engine.
Perry Beadle Flying Boat Tractor Biplane	1914	F	Twickenham/ Cowes/Lake Windemere	Perry Beadle & Co.	Exhibited at Olympia Show. Hull by Saunders, Cowes. Twin chain driven propellers. E.N.V. replaced later by Curtiss engine. Did not fly.

Avro Type D. Biplane.

Avro Duigan Type Biplane.

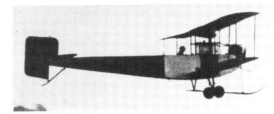

Avro Type E. Biplane.

B.E.2 Biplane.

Eardley Billing Biplane.

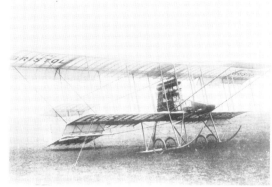

Bristol Boxkite Biplane.

Bristol Challenger-England Biplane.

Cody Type IC.

Cody Type IIB.

Fritz Monoplane.

Grahame-White Biplane.

Howard Wright Monoplane at Olympia Aero Show 1910.

Howard Wright Monoplane. Warwick Wright at Brooklands.

Howard Wright Monoplane.
T.O.M.Sopwith teaching himself to fly.

Howard Wright Biplane without wing extensions.

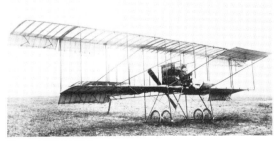

Howard Wright Biplane.
T.O.M.Sopwith Baron de forest aircraft.

Howard Wright Biplane in New Zealand. Brothers L.and V.Walsh
of Auckland.

Lane Monoplane. ▲

Molesworth Triplane.

Neale 6. Monoplane.

Mulliner 2. Knyplane.

Perry Beadle Flying Boat. ◆

Aircraft Type	Date	E.N.V. Type	Aerodrome or Factory	Pilot/Owner	Remarks
Piffard 1 & 2 Pusher Biplane	1909-10	D	Ealing/Shoreham	H Piffard	No 2 was similar to No1 but less tailwheels and with ailerons on the top wing.
Piffard 3 Hydro Biplane	1911	D	Shoreham	H Piffard	A new design of biplane with shot-span lower wing using the earlier engine. Built as a seaplane with a main float and stabilising floats.
Piffard 4 Hydro Biplane	1912	D	Shoreham	H Piffard	A reconstruction of No 3 as a seaplane with twin main floats and single tail float with 2-bay wings and extensions. Engine, radiator etc. now in London Science Museum.
Sanders 2 Pusher Biplane	1911	F	Beccles/ Croydon	Sanders Aeroplane Co. London Aeroplane & Navigation Co.	Reconstruction of Sanders 1. Originally fitted with Alvaston & Brooke engines.
S.E.1 Pusher Biplane	June - 18 Aug.1911	F	Farnborough	Factory	Mainly flown by G de Havilland. Destroyed in fatal crash - Lt. T Ridge
Short S27 Pusher Biplane	1910 June-July	F	Eastchurch	C Grace	Engine now in replica S29 aircraft Cole Palen, New York.
Short S29 Pusher Biplane	1910 - Nov.-Dec.	F	Eastchurch	C Grace	Lost over Channel after initial unsuccessful attempt for Baron de Forest prize by C Grace.
Short S32 Tractor Biplane	1910-11	F	Eastchurch	C Grace	Being constructed when C Grace lost. Rebuilt as S36 with 70 HP Gnome
Skinner Tractor Monoplane	Aug. 1911	F	Brooklands	Skinner	Constructed by Mulliners, Clapham Junction.
Swann Tractor Monoplane	1909	D	Longbridge/ Aintree	S Swann	Constructed by Austin Motor Co. Flight attempt at Aintree in contest for Liverpool to Manchester flight.
Swann Pusher Biplane	1910	D	Crosby/Ravens- worth Westmorland	S Swann	Reconstruction of Monoplane. Destroyed in July at Kings Meaburn after several attempts at flight
Weiss No. 2 Tractor Monoplane	Dec. 1910	D	Brooklands	G England	Named Sylvia. Crashed in sewage farm Brooklands.

Piffard No.1. Biplane (No.2 similar).

Piffard No.3. Hydro-Biplane.

Piffard No.4. Hydro-Biplane.

Sanders No.2 Biplane.

S.E.1. Biplane.

Short S.27 Biplane. S.29 was similar but had wing extensions.

Swann Monoplane.

Weiss No.2 Monoplane.

Skinner Monoplane.

Short S.36 with Gnome engine was evolved from S.32 with E.N.V. Type F for C.S.Grace. No Photographs exist of S.32 which was abandoned after Grace was lost. S.36 was reconstructed for Mc Clean and is themachine referred to by Grace in November 1910. "Mr.Cecil Gracewhen accused of being about to bring out an entirely new and original machine, said that he certainly had a machine under construction which was, in general appearance, not like any well-known machine, but that in detail it really combined what he considered to be the good points of a variety of other machines." The Aero 16.11.1910.

Swann Biplane.

Some European Aircraft with E.N.V. Engines

Aircraft Type	Date	E.N.V. Type	Remarks
Bleriot Type XII Monoplane	1909-10	D & F (Also FA by Bleriot)	Several of this type were built. Grahame-White bought No. 2 named "White Eagle" and gained his first experience of flying with it at Issy-les-Moulineaux and Pau before bringing it to England. Sold to Duke of Westminster and Col. Laycock in June 1910 and donated to the War Office. Crashed in November. Engine used in S.E.1.
Dufaux Biplane	1910-11	F	Built in Geneva by Dufaux Brothers. Four supplied to Swiss Army with either Antoinette or E.N.V. engines.
Farman Pusher Biplane	1910-11	F	Many built with various engines. Grahame-White operated a British-built Farman at Brooklands and and Hendon with an E.N.V.
Turcat-Mery-Rougier	1910	F	One of a number of Continental aircraft using the E.N.V. It was shown at the Paris Aero Show in October 1910 but gained little success in the hands of pilot Rougier.
Voisin Boxkite Pusher Biplane	1908-10	C & F (Probably A also)	Built in large numbers with various engines but considerable number used E.N.V. In England Voisins were bought by Moore-Brabazon and Moreing, the former making the first official flight by an Englishman in April/May 1909 on the Isle of Sheppey. The type was soon superseded by more advanced types with improved control and performance.

Blériot Type XII. *Original machine with E.N.V. Type D engine.*

Blériot Type XII. *Later version at the Paris Show October 1909 with Type F engine.*

Blériot XII. ' White Eagle' of Grahame-White.

Farman Biplane.

Turcat-Mery-Rougier Biplane. *France.*

Dufaux Biplane *made in Switzerland.*

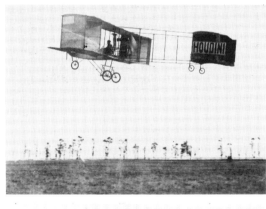

Voisin Biplane. *The first aircraft to fly in Australia in 1910 flown by Houdini (Ehrlich Weiss).*

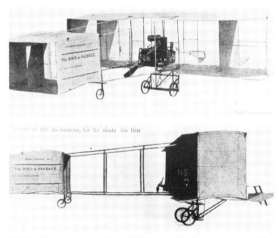

Voisin Biplane owned by J.T.C.Moore-Brabazon *and used by him to become the first Briton to fly in Britain.*

Some Airships with E.N.V. Engines

Name	Date	E.N.V. Type	Aerodrome or Factory	Pilot/Owner	Remarks
Moreing Non-rigid Airship. Also known as Healey and Roberts. Envelope believed by Spencer & Sons (20,000 cu. ft. cap).	Aug. 1909	C	Dagenham Aeronautical Soc. Experimental Ground).	C A Moreing. Healey & Roberts engineers of the Australian Electrical Co.	Unmanned radio-controlled airship for military purposes. Trials discontinued after damage during inflation by Royal Engineers. 100/120 HP engine reported fitted but more likely the current Type C.
Willows No. 5 Non-rigid airship. (50,000 cu.ft. cap).	Nov. 1913- Mar. 1914	F	Hendon	E T Willows	Damaged in shed and deflated.
Marshall-Fox Rigid Airship (108,000 cu.ft.cap)	1914-1915	F (plus one 125 HP Green)	Barking	Marshall-Fox Co. T R MacMechan (US) promoter and W R Kamp (US) designer.	Under construction in Nov. 1915. Made of wood - mostly 5 ply. 2 engines driving 4 x 4 blade outboard propellers by non-stretch cable drive. To lift 4 crew and armament. Not completed.
Wellman non-rigid Airship. America (345,000 cu.ft.cap)	1910	F (plus one 75 HP Lorraine-Dietrich	Atlantic City	Walter Wellman (US) owner. Melvin Vaniman (US) engineer.	Airship lost after being abandoned during attempt to cross Atlantic. Crew saved by lifeboat. Enlarged from America L.A.

Willows No.5 Non-rigid

The Marshall-Fox Rigid Airship built mainly of wood under construction.

Wellman 'America' Non-rigid.

Surviving E.N.V. Engines

The records of engine production are no longer available but it is probable that something between one and two hundred of all types were made by the two factories and of these six are known to be still in existence. Cody's French-made Type C (Series 1 No. 3) is still owned by the Cody family and as far as is known is the only one of this early type still in existence. A French-made Type D (Series 2 No. 2) which was used by H Piffard in two aircraft of his own design at Ealing and Shoreham in 1910-11 is now in the Science Museum in London and also in the museum's possession is the Type F, previously on exhibition, which was donated by O C Morison. (Plate stamped No. 111. 1910). The Type F (Series 1 No. 4) originally used by Cecil Grace was discovered by the author in 1964 and was rebuilt and tested before being passed onto Cole Palen for use in his replica Short S29. The engine was obtained from the Fox family and is believed to have been that used in the trials at Barking connected with the partly completed Marshall-Fox airship. A Type FA (Series 3 No. 6) used by Bleriot in a Type No. XII was on display in 1969 at the Musee de L'Air at Chalais Meudon and an E.N.V. Type F (Series 1 No. —) is in the possession of the Narodni Tecknicke Muzeum in Prague.

Famous users of E.N.V. engines,
both competitors in the Baron de Forest contest.

T.O.M.Sopwith, the winner at Brooklands in his E.N.V. powered Howard Wright with increased fuel capacity as prepared for the contest.

C.S.Grace, loser, seen on the day he was lost in the channel, 22 December 1910, preparing to leave Dover, Stowing the starting handle of the E.N.V. in the Short S.29 is a youthful Joe Gascoyne.

INDEX

(Bold page numbers indicate illustrations)